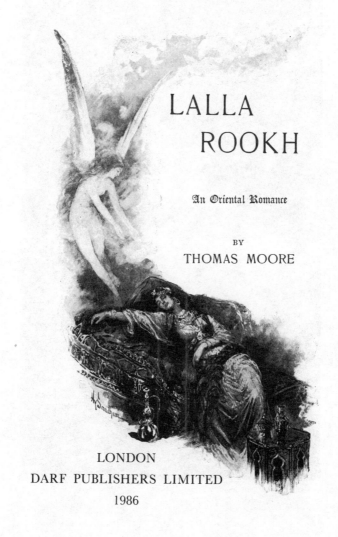

LALLA ROOKH

An Oriental Romance

BY

THOMAS MOORE

LONDON
DARF PUBLISHERS LIMITED
1986

CONTENTS

FIRST PUBLISHED 1901
NEW IMPRESSION 1986

ISBN 1 85077 148 0

Printed and bound in Great Britain
by A. Wheaton & Co. Ltd, Exeter, Devon

MOORE'S HOUSE, IN WHICH LALLA ROOKH WAS WRITTEN.

LIST OF ILLUSTRATIONS.

VII

LIST OF ILLUSTRATIONS.

IN the eleventh year of the reign of
Aurungzebe, Abdalla, King of the
Lesser Bucharia, a lineal descendant
from the Great Zingis, having abdi-

cated the throne in favour of his son, set out on a pilgrimage to the Shrine of the Prophet, and, passing
into India through the delightful valley of Cashmere,
rested for a short time at Delhi on his way.   He
was entertained by Aurungzebe in a style of magnificent hospitality, worthy alike of the visitor and
the host, and was afterward escorted with the same
splendour to Surat, where he embarked for Arabia.
During the stay of the Royal Pilgrim at Delhi, a
marriage was agreed upon between the Prince, his
son, and the youngest daughter of the Emperor,
Lalla Rookh, — a princess described by the poets of
her time as more beautiful than Leila, Shirine, De-
wildé, or any of those heroines whose names and loves
embellish the songs of Persia and Hindostan.   It was
intended that the nuptials should be celebrated at
Cashmere; where the young King, as soon as the
cares of empire would permit, was to meet, for the first
time, his lovely bride, and, after a few months' repose
in that enchanting valley, conduct her over the snowy
hills into Bucharia.

The day of Lalla Rookh's departure from Delhi was
as splendid as sunshine and pageantry could make it.
The bazaars and baths were all covered with the richest tapestry; hundreds of gilded barges upon the
Jumna floated with their banners shining in the water;
while through the streets troops of beautiful children
went strewing the most delicious flowers around, as in
that Persian festival called the Scattering of the Roses,
till every part of the city was as fragrant as if a caravan of musk from Khoten had passed through it.   The

Princess, having taken leave of her kind father, who at parting hung a carnelian of Yemen around her neck, on which was inscribed a verse from the Koran, and having sent a considerable present to the Fakirs, who kept up the Perpetual Lamp in her sister's tomb, meekly ascended the palankeen prepared for her; and while Aurungzebe stood to take a last look from his balcony, the procession moved slowly on the road to Lahore.

Seldom had the Eastern World seen a cavalcade so superb. From the gardens in the suburbs to the imperial palace, it was one unbroken line of splendour. The gallant appearance of the Rajas and Mogul lords, distinguished by those insignia of the Emperor's favour, the feathers of the egret of Cashmere in their turbans and the small silver-rimmed kettle-drums at the bows of their saddles; the costly armour of their cavaliers, who vied, on this occasion, with the guards of the great Kedar Khan, in the brightness of their silver battle-axes and the massiveness of their maces of gold; the glittering of the gilt pineapples on the tops of the palankeens; the embroidered trappings of the elephants, bearing on their backs small turrets, in the shape of little antique temples, within which the ladies of Lalla Rookh lay, as it were, enshrined; the rose-coloured veils of the Princess's own sumptuous litter, at the front of which a fair young female slave sat fanning her through the curtains, with feathers of the Argus pheasant's wing; and the lovely troop of Tartarian and Cashmerian maids of honour, whom the young King had sent to accompany his bride, and

who rode on each side
of the litter, upon small
Arabian horses ; — all was
brilliant, tasteful, and magnificent, and pleased even
the critical and fastidious
Fadladeen, Great Nazir or
Chamberlain of the Haram,
who was borne in his pal-
ankeen immediately after
the Princess, and con-
sidered himself not the
least important personage
of the pageant.

Fadladeen was a judge of
everything, — from the pen-
cilling of a Circassian's eyelids to the deepest questions
of science and literature,
from the mixture of a conserve of rose-leaves to the

composition of an epic poem; and such influence had
his opinion upon the various tastes of the day, that
all the cooks and poets of Delhi stood in awe of
him. His political conduct and opinions were founded
upon that line of Sadi: "Should the Prince at noon-
day say, 'It is night,' declare that you behold the moon
and stars." And his zeal for religion, of which Aurungzebe was a munificent protector, was about as
disinterested as that of the goldsmith who fell in love
with the diamond eyes of the idol of Jaghernaut.

During the first days of their journey, Lalla Rookh,
who had passed all her life within the shadow of the
royal Gardens of Delhi, found enough in the beauty of
the scenery through which they passed to interest her
mind and delight her imagination; and when, at evening or in the heat of the day, they turned off from the
high-road to those retired and romantic places which
had been selected for her encampments, — sometimes
on the banks of a small rivulet, as clear as the waters
of the Lake of Pearl; sometimes under the sacred
shade of a banyan-tree, from which the view opened
upon a glade covered with antelopes; and often in
those hidden, embowered spots, described by one from
the Isles of the West, as "places of melancholy, delight, and safety, where all the company around was
wild peacocks and turtle-doves," — she felt a charm in
these scenes, so lovely and so new to her, which for
a time made her indifferent to every other amusement.
But Lalla Rookh was young, and the young love vari-
ety; nor could the conversation of her Ladies and the
Great Chamberlain, Fadladeen (the only persons, of

course, admitted to her pavilion), sufficiently enliven
those many vacant hours which were devoted neither
to the pillow nor the palankeen.   There was a little
Persian slave who sung sweetly to the Vina, and who
now and then lulled the Princess to sleep with the
ancient ditties of her country, about the loves of
Wamak and Ezra, the fair-haired Zal and his mistress
Rodahver, not forgetting the combat of Rustam with
the terrible White Demon.   At other times she was
amused by those graceful dancing-girls of Delhi, who
had been permitted by the Brahmins of the Great
Pagoda to attend her, much to the horror of the good
Mussulman Fadladeen, who could see nothing graceful
or agreeable in idolaters, and to whom the very tinkling of their golden anklets was an abomination.

But these and many other diver-
sions were repeated till they
lost all their charm, and

the nights and noondays were beginning to move
heavily, when at length it was recollected that, among
the attendants sent by the bridegroom, was a young
poet of Cashmere, much celebrated throughout the valley for his manner of reciting the stories of the East,
on whom his Royal Master had conferred the privi-
lege of being admitted to the pavilion of the Princess, that he might help to beguile the tediousness of
the journey by some of his most agreeable recitals.
At the mention of a poet Fadladeen elevated his
critical eyebrows, and, having refreshed his faculties
with a dose of that delicious opium which is distilled
from the black poppy of the Thebais, gave orders
for the minstrel to be forthwith introduced into the
presence.

The Princess, who had once in her life seen a poet
from behind the screens of gauze in her father's hall,
and had conceived from that specimen no very favourable ideas of the Caste, expected but little in this new
exhibition to interest her; she felt inclined, however,
to alter her opinion on the very first appearance of
Feramorz. He was a youth about Lalla Rookh's own
age, and graceful as that idol of women, Crishna, —
such as he appears to their young imaginations, heroic,
beautiful, breathing music from his very eyes, and
exalting the religion of his worshippers into love. His
dress was simple, yet not without some marks of
costliness; and the Ladies of the Princess were not
long in discovering that the cloth which encircled his
high Tartarian cap was of the most delicate kind that
the shawl-goats of Tibet supply. Here and there, too,

over his vest, which was
confined by a flowered
girdle of Kashan, hung

strings of fine pearl, disposed with an air of studied negligence; nor did the exquisite embroidery of his sandals escape the observation of these fair critics, who, however they might give way to Fadladeen upon the unimportant topics of religion and government, had the spirit of martyrs in everything relating to such momentous matters as jewels and embroidery.

For the purpose of relieving the pauses of recitation by music, the young Cashmerian held in his hand a kitar, — such as, in old times, the Arab maids of the West used to listen to by moonlight in the gardens of the Alhambra, — and having promised, with much humility, that the story he was about to relate was founded on the adventures of that Veiled Prophet of Khorassan who, in the year of the Hegira 163, created such alarm throughout the Eastern Empire, made an obeisance to the Princess, and thus began :

THE
VEILED
PROPHET
OF KHORASSAN

THE

VEILED PROPHET OF KHORASSAN.

IN that delightful Province of the Sun,
   The first of Persian lands he shines upon,
Where, all the loveliest children of his beam,
Flowerets and fruits blush over every stream,
And, fairest of all streams, the Murga roves
Among Meron's bright palaces and groves, —
There, on that throne to which the blind belief
Of millions raised him, sat the Prophet-Chief,
The Great Mokanna.   O'er his features hung
The Veil, the Silver Veil, which he had flung
In mercy there, to hide from mortal sight
His dazzling brow, till man could bear its light.
For far less luminous, his votaries said,
Were e'en the gleams, miraculously shed
O'er Moussa's cheek, when down the mount he trod,
All glowing from the presence of his God !

On either side, with ready hearts and hands,
His chosen guard of bold believers stands, —
Young fire-eyed disputants, who deem their swords,
On points of faith, more eloquent than words, —
And such their zeal, there's not a youth with brand
Uplifted there, but, at the Chief's command,
Would make his own devoted heart its sheath,
And bless the lips that doom'd so dear a death !

In hatred to the caliph's hue of night,
Their vesture, helms and all, is snowy white;
Their weapons various, — some, equipp'd for speed,
With javelins of the light Kathaian reed,
Or bows of buffalo horn, and shining quivers
Fill'd with the stems that bloom on Iran's rivers,
While some, for war's more terrible attacks,
Wield the huge mace, and ponderous battle-axe;
And, as they wave aloft in
    morning's beam
The milk-white plumage of
    their helms, they seem
Like a chenar-tree grove
    when winter throws
O'er all its tufted heads his
    feathering snows.

Between the porphyry pillars, that uphold
The rich moresque-work of the roof of gold,
Aloft the haram's curtain'd galleries rise,
Where, through the silken network, glancing eyes,
From time to time, like sudden gleams that glow
Through autumn clouds, shine o'er the pomp below. —
What impious tongue, ye blushing saints, would dare
To hint that aught but Heaven hath placed you there?
Or that the loves of this light world could bind,
In their gross chain, your Prophet's soaring mind?
No, — wrongful thought! — commission'd from above
To people Eden's bowers with shapes of love
(Creatures so bright, that the same lips and eyes
They wear on earth will serve in Paradise),
There to recline among heaven's native maids,
And crown th' elect with bliss that never fades, —
Well hath the Prophet-Chief his bidding done;
And every beauteous race beneath the sun,
From those who kneel at Brahma's burning founts,
To the fresh nymphs bounding o'er Yemen's mounts;
From Persia's eyes of full and fawn-like ray,
To the small, half-shut glances of Kathay;
And Georgia's bloom, and Azab's darker smiles,
And the gold ringlets of the Western Isles, —
All, all are there; each land its flower hath given,
To form that fair young Nursery for Heaven!

But why this pageant now? this arm'd array?
What triumph crowds the rich divan to-day
With turban'd heads, of every hue and race,
Bowing before that veil'd and awful face,

Like tulip-beds of different shape and
   dyes,
Bending beneath th' invisible west-
   wind's sighs?

What new-
   made
   mystery now,
   for Faith to
   sign,
And blood to seal, as
   genuine and divine?
What dazzling mimicry
   of God's own power
Hath the bold Prophet
   plann'd to grace this hour?
Not such the pageant now, though not less proud:
Yon warrior youth, advancing from the crowd,

With silver bow, with belt
    of broider'd crape,
And fur-bound bonnet of
    Bucharian shape,
So fiercely beautiful in
    form and eye,
Like war's wild planet in
    a summer sky, —
That youth to-day — a
    proselyte worth
    hordes
Of cooler spirits and less
    practised swords —
Is come to join, all bravery and belief,
The creed and standard of the heaven-sent Chief.

    Though few his years, the west already knows
Young Azim's fame; beyond th' Olympian snows,
Ere manhood darken'd o'er his downy cheek,
O'erwhelm'd in fight, and captive to the Greek,

He linger'd there, till peace dissolved his chains; —
Oh! who could, e'en in bondage, tread the plains
Of glorious Greece, nor feel his spirit rise
Kindling within him? who, with heart and eyes,
Could walk where Liberty had been, nor see
The shining footprints of her Deity,
Nor feel those god-like breathings in the air,
Which mutely told her spirit had been there?
Not he, that youthful warrior, — no, too well
For his soul's quiet work'd th' awakening spell!
And now, returning to his own dear land,
Full of those dreams of good that, vainly grand,
Haunt the young heart, — proud views of human-
        kind,
Of men to gods exalted and refined;
False views, like that horizon's fair deceit,
Where earth and heaven but *seem*, alas! to meet, —
Soon as he heard an Arm Divine was raised
To right the nations, and beheld emblazed
On the white flag Mokanna's host unfurl'd,
Those words of sunshine, " Freedom to the World,"
At once his faith, his sword, his soul, obey'd
Th' inspiring summons; every chosen blade,
That fought beneath that banner's sacred text,
Seem'd doubly edged, for this world and the next;
And ne'er did Faith with her smooth bandage bind
Eyes more devoutly willing to be blind
In virtue's cause, never was soul inspired
With livelier trust in what it most desired,
Than his, th' enthusiast there, who kneeling, pale
With pious awe, before that Silver Veil,

Believes the form to which he bends his knee,
Some pure, redeeming angel, sent to free
This fetter'd world from every bond and stain,
And bring its primal glories back again !

Low as young Azim knelt, that motley crowd
Of all earth's nations sunk the knee and bow'd,
With shouts of " Alla ! " echoing long and loud ;
While high in air, above the Prophet's head,
Hundreds of banners, to the sunbeam spread,
Waved, like the wings of the white birds that fan
The flying throne of star-taught Soliman !
Then thus he spoke : " Stranger, though new the frame
Thy soul inhabits now, I've tracked its flame
For many an age, in every chance and change,
Of that existence through whose varied range —
As through a torch-race, where, from hand to hand,
The flying youths transmit their shining brand —
From frame to frame th' unextinguish'd soul
Rapidly passes, till it reach the goal !

" Nor think 'tis only the gross spirits, warm'd
With duskier fire and for earth's medium form'd,
That run this course ; beings the most divine
Thus deign through dark mortality to shine.
Such was the essence that in Adam dwelt,
To which all heaven, except the Proud One, knelt ;
Such the refined intelligence that glow'd
In Moussa's frame, and, thence descending, flow'd
Through many a Prophet's breast, — in Issa shone,
And in Mohammed burn'd, till, hastening on,

(As a bright river that, from fall to fall
In many a maze descending, bright through all,
Finds some fair region where, each labyrinth past,
In one full lake of light it rests at last!)
That Holy Spirit, settling calm and free
From lapse or shadow, centres all in me!"

Again throughout th' assembly, at these words,
Thousands of voices rung; the warriors' swords
Were pointed up to heaven; a sudden wind
In th' open banners play'd, and from behind
Those Persian hangings, that but ill could screen
The haram's loveliness, white hands were seen
Waving embroider'd scarves, whose motion gave
A perfume forth, — like those the Houris wave,
When beckoning to their bowers th' Immortal Brave.

"But these," pursued the Chief, "are truths sublime,
That claim a holier mood and calmer time
Than earth allows us now; this sword must first
The darkling prison-house of mankind burst,
Ere peace can visit them, or truth let in
Her wakening daylight on a world of sin!
But then, celestial warriors, then, when all
Earth's shrines and thrones before our banner fall;
When the glad slave shall at these feet lay down
His broken chain, the tyrant lord his crown,
The priest his book, the conqueror his wreath,
And from the lips of Truth one mighty breath
Shall, like a whirlwind, scatter in its breeze
That whole dark pile of human mockeries, —

Then shall the
reign of Mind
commence on
earth,
A n d   starting
fresh, as from
a second birth,
Man, in the sunshine
of the world's new
spring,
Shall   walk
transparent,
like   some
holy thing!
Then, too, your
Prophet from his angel brow
Shall cast the Veil, that hides its splendours now,
And gladden'd earth shall through her wide expanse
Bask in the glories of this countenance!

"For thee, young war-
　　rior, welcome! —
　　thou hast yet
Some tasks to learn, some frailties to
　　forget,
Ere the white war-plume o'er thy brow can wave;
But, once my own, mine all till in the grave!"

The pomp is at an end, — the crowds are gone,
Each ear and heart still haunted by the tone
Of that deep voice, which thrill'd like Alla's own!
The young all dazzled by the plumes and lances,
The glittering throne, and haram's half-caught glances;
The old deep pondering on the promised reign
Of peace and truth; and all the female train
Ready to risk their eyes, could they but gaze
A moment on that brow's miraculous blaze!

But there was one among the chosen maids
Who blush'd behind the gallery's silken shades,
One to whose soul the pageant of to-day
Has been like death ; — you saw her pale dismay,
Ye wandering sisterhood, and heard the burst
Of exclamation from her lips, when first
She saw that youth, too well, too dearly known,
Silently kneeling at the Prophet's throne.

Ah, Zelica ! there *was* a time when bliss
Shone o'er thy heart from every look of his ;
When but to see him, hear him, breathe the air
In which he dwelt, was thy soul's fondest prayer !
When round him hung such a perpetual spell,
Whate'er he did, none ever did so well.
Too happy days ! when, if he touch'd a flower
Or gem of thine, 'twas sacred from that hour ;
When thou didst study him, till every tone
And gesture and dear look became thy own, —
Thy voice like his, the changes of his face
In thine reflected with still lovelier grace,
Like echo, sending back sweet music, fraught
With twice th' aerial sweetness it had brought !
Yet now he comes, — brighter than even he
E'er beam'd before, — but, ah ! not bright for thee :
No, — dread, unlook'd for, like a visitant
From th' other world, he comes as if to haunt
Thy guilty soul with dreams of lost delight,
Long lost to all but memory's aching sight ;
Sad dreams ! as when the Spirit of our youth
Returns in sleep, sparkling with all the truth

And innocence once ours, and leads us back,
In mournful mockery, o'er the shining track
Of our young life, and points out every ray
Of hope and peace we've lost upon the way!

Once happy pair! — in proud Bokhara's groves,
Who had not heard of their first youthful loves?
Born by that ancient flood, which from its spring
In the Dark Mountains swiftly wandering,
Enrich'd by every pilgrim brook that shines
With relics from Bucharia's ruby mines,
And, lending to the Caspian half its strength,
In the cold Lake of Eagles sinks at length, —
There, on the banks of that bright river born,
The flowers, that hung above its wave at morn,
Bless'd not the waters, as they murmur'd by,
With holier scent and lustre, than the sigh
And virgin glance of first affection cast
Upon their youth's smooth current, as it pass'd!
But war disturb'd this vision: far away
From her fond eyes, summon'd to join th' array
Of Persia's warriors on the hills of Thrace,
The youth exchanged his sylvan dwelling-place
For the rude tent and war-field's deathful clash;
His Zelica's sweet glances for the flash
Of Grecian wild-fire, and Love's gentle chains
For bleeding bondage on Byzantium's plains.

Month after month, in widowhood of soul
Drooping, the maiden saw two summers roll
Their suns away, — but, ah! how cold and dim
Even summer suns, when not beheld with him!

From time to time ill-omen'd rumours came
(Like spirit tongues, muttering the sick man's name
Just ere he dies); at length, those sounds of dread
Fell withering on her soul, "Azim is dead!"
Oh, grief beyond all other griefs, when fate
First leaves the young heart lone and desolate
In the wide world, without that only tie
For which it loved to live or fear'd to die, —
Lorn as the hung-up lute, that ne'er hath spoken
Since the sad day its master-chord was broken!

Fond maid, the sorrow of her soul was such,
E'en reason sunk, blighted beneath its touch;
And though, erelong, her sanguine spirit rose
Above the first dead pressure of its woes,
Though health and bloom return'd, the delicate chain
Of thought, once tangled, never clear'd again.
Warm, lively, soft as in youth's happiest day,
The mind was still all there, but turn'd astray, —
A wandering bark, upon whose pathway shone
All stars of heaven, except the guiding one!
Again she smiled, nay, much and brightly smiled;
But 'twas a lustre strange, unreal, wild;
And when she sung to her lute's touching strain,
'Twas like the notes, half ecstasy, half pain,
The bulbul utters, ere her soul depart,
When, vanquished by some minstrel's powerful art,
She dies upon the lute whose sweetness broke her heart!

Such was the mood in which that mission found
Young Zelica, — that mission, which around

The eastern world, in every region blest
With woman's smile, sought out its loveliest,
To grace that galaxy of lips and eyes
Which the Veil'd Prophet destined for the skies ! —
And such quick welcome as a spark receives
Dropp'd on a bed of autumn's wither'd leaves,
Did every tale of these enthusiasts find
In the wild maiden's sorrow-blighted mind.
All fire, at once the maddening zeal she caught; —
Elect of Paradise ! blest, rapturous thought;
Predestined bride, in heaven's eternal dome,
Of some brave youth — ha ! durst they say " of *some* ?"
No, — of the one, one only object traced
In her heart's core too deep to be effaced ;
The one whose memory, fresh as life, is twined
With every broken link of her lost mind, —
Whose image lives, though reason's self be wreck'd,
Safe 'mid the ruins of her intellect !

   Alas, poor Zelica ! it needed all
The fantasy which held thy mind in thrall,
To see in that gay haram's glowing maids
A sainted colony for Eden's shades ;
Or dream that he — of whose unholy flame
Thou wert too soon the victim — shining came
From Paradise, to people its pure sphere
With souls like thine, which he hath ruin'd here !
No, — had not reason's light totally set,
And left thee dark, thou hadst an amulet
In the loved image, graven on thy heart,
Which would have saved thee from the tempter's art,

And kept alive, in all its bloom of breath,
That purity, whose fading is love's death!
But lost, inflamed, a restless zeal took place
Of the mild virgin's still and feminine grace;
First of the Prophet's favourites, proudly first
In zeal and charms, too well th' impostor nursed
Her soul's delirium, in whose active flame,
Thus lighting up a young, luxuriant frame,
He saw more potent sorceries to bind
To his dark yoke the spirits of mankind,
More subtle chains than hell itself e'er twined.
No art was spared, no witchery; all the skill
His demons taught him was employ'd to fill
Her mind with gloom and ecstasy by turns, —
That gloom through which frenzy but fiercer burns;
That ecstasy which from the depth of sadness
Glares like the maniac's moon, whose light is mad-
    ness!

'Twas from a brilliant banquet, where the sound
Of poesy and music breathed around,
Together picturing to her mind and ear
The glories of that heaven, her destined sphere,
Where all was pure, where every stain that lay
Upon the spirit's light should pass away,
And, realising more than youthful love
E'er wish'd or dream'd, she should for ever rove
Through fields of fragrance by her Azim's side,
His own bless'd, purified, eternal bride! —
'Twas from a scene, a witching trance, like this,
He hurried her away, yet breathing bliss,

To the dim charnel-house; — through all its steams
Of damp and death, led only by those gleams
Which foul Corruption lights, as with design
To show the gay and proud *she* too can shine! —
And, passing on through upright ranks of dead,
Which to the maiden, doubly crazed by dread,
Seem'd, through the bluish death-light round them cast,
To move their lips in mutterings as she pass'd, —
There, in that awful place, when each had quaff'd
And pledged in silence such a fearful draught,
Such — oh! the look and taste of that red bowl
Will haunt her till she dies, — he bound her soul
By a dark oath, in hell's own language framed,
Never, while earth his mystic presence claim'd,

While the blue arch of day hung o'er
　　them both,
Never, by that all-imprecating oath,
In joy or sorrow from his side to
　　sever.
She swore, and the wide charnel
　　echo'd, " Never, never ! "

From that
　　dread hour,
　　entirely,
　　wildly given
To him and
　　— she be-
　　lieved, lost
　　maid ! — to
　　Heaven ;
Her brain,
　　her heart,
　　her pas-
　　sions, all
　　inflamed,
How proud
　　she stood,
　　when in full
　　haram
　　named
The Priestess
　　of the
　　Faith ! —
　　how flash'd
　　her eyes

With light, alas! that was not of the skies,
When round in trances only less than hers,
She saw the haram kneel, her prostrate worshippers!
Well might Mokanna think that form alone
Had spells enough to make the world his own, —
Light, lovely limbs, to which the spirit's play
Gave motion, airy as the dancing spray
When from its stem the small bird wings away!
Lips in whose rosy labyrinth, when she smiled,
The soul was lost; and blushes, swift and wild
As are the momentary meteors sent
Across th' uncalm but beauteous firmament.
And then her look! — oh! where's the heart so wise,
Could unbewilder'd meet those matchless eyes?
Quick, restless, strange, but exquisite withal,
Like those of angels, just before their fall;
Now shadow'd with the shames of earth, now cross'd
By glimpses of the heaven her heart had lost;
In every glance there broke, without control,
The flashes of a bright but troubled soul,
Where sensibility still wildly play'd,
Like lightning, round the ruins it had made!

And such was now young Zelica, — so changed
From her who, some years since, delighted ranged
The almond groves that shade Bokhara's tide,
All life and bliss, with Azim by her side!
So alter'd was she now, this festal day,
When, 'mid the proud divan's dazzling array,
The vision of that youth, whom she had loved,
And wept as dead, before her breathed and moved;

When — bright, she thought, as if from Eden's track
But half-way trodden, he had wander'd back
Again to earth, glistening with Eden's light —
Her beauteous Azim shone before her sight.

O Reason ! who shall say what spells renew,
When least we look for it, thy broken clew ?
Through what small vistas o'er the darken'd brain
Thy intellectual daybeam bursts again ?
And how, like forts, to which beleaguerers win
Unhoped-for entrance through some friend within,
One clear idea, waken'd in the breast
By memory's magic, lets in all the rest ?
Would it were thus, unhappy girl, with thee !
But, though light came, it came but partially ;
Enough to show the maze in which thy sense
Wander'd about, but not to guide it thence ;
Enough to glimmer o'er the yawning wave,
But not to point the harbour which might save.
Hours of delight and peace, long left behind,
With that dear form came rushing o'er her mind ;
But, oh ! to think how deep her soul had gone
In shame and falsehood since those moments shone ;
And, then, her oath, — *there* madness lay again,
And, shuddering, back she sunk into a chain
Of mental darkness, as if blest to flee
From light, whose every glimpse was agony !
Yet *one* relief this glance of former years
Brought, mingled with its pain, — tears, floods of tears,
Long frozen at her heart, but now like rills
Let loose in spring-time from the snowy hills,

And gushing warm, after a
   sleep of frost,
Through valleys where their
   flow had long been lost!

Sad and subdued, for the
   first time her frame
Trembled with horror, when
   the summons came
(A summons proud and rare, which all but she,
And she, till now, had heard with ecstasy)
To meet Mokanna at his place of prayer,
A garden oratory, cool and fair,
By the stream's side, where still at close of day
The Prophet of the Veil retired to pray;
Sometimes alone, but oftener far with one,
One chosen nymph, to share his orison.

   Of late none found such favour in his sight
As the young Priestess; and though, since that night

When the death-caverns echo'd every tone
Of the dire oath that made her all his own,
Th' impostor, sure of his infatuate prize,
Had, more than once, thrown off his soul's disguise,
And utter'd such unheavenly, monstrous things,
As e'en across the desperate wanderings
Of a weak intellect, whose lamp was out,
Threw startling shadows of dismay and doubt,
Yet zeal, ambition, her tremendous vow,
The thought, still haunting her, of that bright brow
Whose blaze, as yet from mortal eye conceal'd,
Would soon, proud triumph! be to her reveal'd,
To her alone; and then the hope, most dear,
Most wild of all, that her transgression here
Was but a passage through earth's grosser fire,
From which the spirit would at last aspire,
Even purer than before, — as perfumes rise
Through flame and smoke, most welcome to the skies,—
And that when Azim's fond, divine embrace
Should circle her in heaven, no darkening trace
Would on that bosom he once loved remain,
But all be bright, be pure, be *his* again ! —

Wan and dejected, through the evening dusk,
She now went slowly to that small kiosk,
Where, pondering alone his impious schemes,
Mokanna waited her, too wrapt in dreams
Of the fair-ripening future's rich success,
To heed the sorrow, pale and spiritless,
That sat upon his victim's downcast brow,
Or mark how slow her step, how alter'd now

From the quick, ardent Priestess, whose light bound
Came like a spirit's o'er th' unechoing ground, —
From that wild Zelica, whose every glance
Was thrilling fire, whose every thought a trance !

Upon his couch the Veil'd Mokanna lay,
While lamps around — not such as lend their ray,
Glimmering and cold, to those who nightly pray
In holy Koom, or Mecca's dim arcades,
But brilliant, soft, — such lights as lovely maids

Look loveliest in — shed their luxurious glow
Upon his mystic Veil's white glittering flow.
Beside him, 'stead of beads and books of prayer,
Which the world fondly thought he mused on there,
Stood vases, filled with Kishmee's golden wine,
And the red weepings of the Shiraz vine;
Of which his curtain'd lips full many a draught
Took zealously, as if each drop they quaff'd,
Like Zemzem's Spring of Holiness, had power
To freshen the soul's virtues into flower!
And still he drank and ponder'd, nor could see
Th' approaching maid, so deep his reverie;
At length, with fiendish laugh, like that which broke
From Eblis at the Fall of Man, he spoke :

" Yes, ye vile race, for hell's amusement given,
Too mean for earth, yet claiming kin with Heaven;
God's images, forsooth ! — such gods as he
Whom India serves, the monkey deity;
Ye creatures of a breath, proud things of clay,
To whom if Lucifer, as grandams say,
Refused, though at the forfeit of Heaven's light,
To bend in worship, Lucifer was right ! —
Soon shall I plant this foot upon the neck
Of your foul race, and without fear or check,
Luxuriating in hate, avenge my shame,
My deep-felt, long-nurst loathing of man's name ! —
Soon, at the head of myriads, blind and fierce
As hooded falcons, through the universe
I'll sweep my darkening, desolating way,
Weak man my instrument, curst man my prey !

LR-D

" Ye wise, ye learn'd, who grope your dull way on
By the dim twinkling gleams of ages gone,
Like superstitious thieves, who think the light
From dead men's marrow guides them best at night,
Ye shall have honours, wealth, — yes, sages, yes, —
I know, grave fools, your wisdom's nothingness ;
Undazzled it can track yon starry sphere,
But a gilt stick, a bawble, blinds it here.
How I shall laugh, when trumpeted along,
In lying speech and still more lying song,
By these learn'd slaves, the meanest of the throng ;
Their wits bought up, their wisdom shrunk so small
A sceptre's puny point can wield it all !

" Ye, too, believers of incredible creeds,
Whose faith enshrines the monsters which it breeds ;
Who, bolder even than Nemrod, think to rise,
By nonsense heap'd on nonsense to the skies,
Ye shall have the miracles, aye, sound ones too,
Seen, heard, attested, everything — but true.
Your preaching zealots, too inspired to seek
One grace of meaning for the things they speak ;
Your martyrs, ready to shed out their blood,
For truths too heavenly to be understood ;
And your state priests, sole venders of the lore
That works salvation, — as on Ava's shore,
Where none *but* priests are privileged to trade
In that best marble of which gods are made ; —
They shall have mysteries, — aye, precious stuff
For knaves to thrive by, — mysteries enough ;
Dark, tangled doctrines, dark as fraud can weave,

Which simple votaries shall on trust receive,
While craftier feign belief, till they believe.
A heaven, too, ye must have, ye lords of dust, —
A splendid paradise, — pure souls, ye must :
That Prophet ill sustains his holy call,
Who finds not heavens to suit the tastes of all;
Houris for boys, omniscience for sages,
And wings and glories for all ranks and ages.
Vain things ! — as lust or vanity inspires,
The heaven of each is but what each desires,

And, soul or sense, what-
e'er the object be,
Man would be man to all
eternity !
So let him — Eblis ! grant
this crowning curse,
But keep him what he is,
no hell were worse."

" Oh, my lost soul ! " exclaim'd the shuddering
maid,
Whose ears had drunk
like   poison all he
said.
Mokanna started, — not
abash'd, afraid :
He knew no more of fear
than one who dwells
Beneath the tropics
knows of icicles !

But in those dismal words that reach'd his ear,
" Oh, my lost soul ! " there was a sound so drear,
So like that voice among the sinful dead,
In which the legend o'er hell's gate is read,
That, new as 'twas from her, whom nought could dim
Or sink till now, it startled even him.

" Ha, my fair Priestess ! " thus, with ready wile,
Th' impostor turn'd to greet her, — " thou, whose smile
Hath inspiration in its rosy beam
Beyond the enthusiast's hope or prophet's dream !
Light of the Faith ! who twin'st religion's zeal
So close with love's, men know not which they feel,
Nor which to sigh for, in their trance of heart, —
The heaven thou preachest or the heaven thou art !
What should I be without thee ? without thee
How dull were power, how joyless victory !
Though borne by angels, if that smile of thine
Bless'd not my banner, 'twere but half divine.
But — why so mournful, child ? those eyes, that shone
All life last night — what ! is their glory gone ?
Come, come, — this morn's fatigue hath made them pale,
They want rekindling, — suns themselves would fail,
Did not their comets bring, as I to thee,
From Light's own fount supplies of brilliancy !
Thou seest this cup, — no juice of earth is here,
But the pure waters of that upper sphere,
Whose rills o'er ruby beds and topaz flow,
Catching the gem's bright colour, as they go.

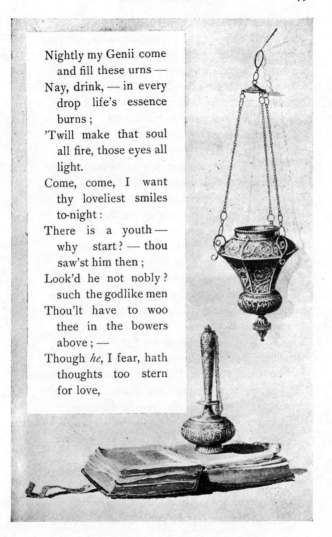

Nightly my Genii come
   and fill these urns —
Nay, drink, — in every
   drop life's essence
   burns ;
'Twill make that soul
   all fire, those eyes all
   light.
Come, come, I want
   thy loveliest smiles
   to-night :
There is a youth —
   why start ? — thou
   saw'st him then ;
Look'd he not nobly ?
   such the godlike men
Thou'lt have to woo
   thee in the bowers
   above ; —
Though *he*, I fear, hath
   thoughts too stern
   for love,

Too ruled by that cold enemy of bliss
The world calls virtue, — we must conquer this ; —
Nay, shrink not, pretty sage ; 'tis not for thee
To scan the maze of heaven's mystery.
The steel must pass through fire, ere it can yield
Fit instruments for mighty hands to wield.
This very night I mean to try the art
Of powerful beauty on that warrior's heart.
All that my haram boasts of bloom and wit,
Of skill and charms, most rare and exquisite,
Shall tempt the boy, — young Mirzala's blue eyes,
Whose sleepy lid like snow on violet lies ;
Arouya's cheeks, warm as a spring-day sun,
And lips that, like the seal of Solomon,
Have magic in their pressure ; Zeba's lute,
And Lilla's dancing feet, that gleam and shoot
Rapid and white as sea-birds o'er the deep ! —
All shall combine their witching powers to steep
My convert's spirit in that softening trance,
From which to heaven is but the next advance, —
That glowing, yielding fusion of the breast,
On which Religion stamps her image best.
But hear me, Priestess ! though each nymph of these
Hath some peculiar, practised power to please,
Some glance or step, which, at the mirror tried,
First charms herself, then all the world beside,
There still wants *one* to make the victory sure,
One who in every look joins every lure ;
Through whom all beauty's beams concentred pass,
Dazzling and warm, as through love's burning-glass,
Whose gentle lips persuade without a word,

Whose words, even when unmeaning, are adored,
Like inarticulate breathings from a shrine,
Which our faith takes for granted are divine !
Such is the nymph we want, all warmth and light,
To crown the rich temptations of to-night ;
Such the refined enchantress that must be
This hero's vanquisher, — and thou art she ! "

With her hands clasp'd, her lips apart and pale,
The maid had stood, gazing upon the Veil
From which these words, like south winds through a
    fence
Of Kerzrah flowers, came filled with pestilence :
So boldly utter'd too ! as if all dread
Of frowns from her, of virtuous frowns, were fled,
And the wretch felt assured that, once plunged in,
Her woman's soul would know no pause in sin !

At first, though mute she listen'd, like a dream
Seem'd all he said ; nor could her mind, whose beam
As yet was weak, penetrate half his scheme.
But when, at length, he uttered, " Thou art she ! "
All flash'd at once, and, shrieking piteously,
" Oh, not for worlds ! " she cried — " Great God ! to
    whom
I once knelt innocent, is this my doom ?
Are all my dreams, my hopes of heavenly bliss,
My purity, my pride, then come to this ? —
To live, the wanton of a fiend ! to be
The pander of his guilt — oh, infamy ! —
And sunk, myself, as low as hell can steep

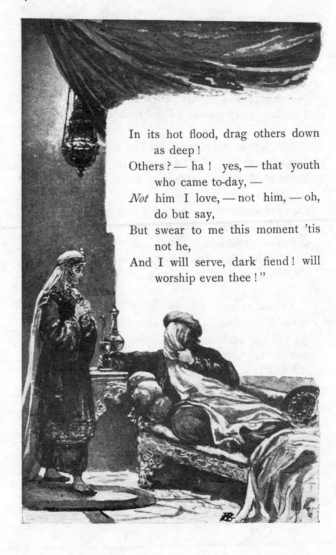

In its hot flood, drag others down
    as deep !
Others ? — ha ! yes, — that youth
    who came to-day, —
Not him I love, — not him, — oh,
    do but say,
But swear to me this moment 'tis
    not he,
And I will serve, dark fiend ! will
    worship even thee ! "

" Beware, young raving thing ! —
  in time beware,
Nor utter what I cannot, must not,
  bear
Even from *thy* lips. Go, try thy lute,
  thy voice ;
The boy must feel their magic, — I
  rejoice
To see those fires, no matter whence
  they rise,
Once more illuming my fair Priestess' eyes ;

And should the youth, whom soon those eyes shall
　warm,
Indeed resemble thy dead lover's form,
So much the happier wilt thou find thy doom,
As one warm lover, full of life and bloom,
Excels ten thousand cold ones in the tomb.
Nay, nay, no frowning, sweet ! those eyes were made
For love, not anger, — I must be obey'd."

"Obey'd ! — 'tis well, — yes, I deserve it all.
On me — on me Heaven's vengeance cannot fall
Too heavily ; but Azim, brave and true
And beautiful, — must *he* be ruin'd too ?
Must *he*, too, glorious as he is, be driven,
A renegade, like me, from love and heaven ?
Like me ? — weak wretch, I wrong him, — not like me ;
No, — he's all truth and strength and purity !
Fill up your maddening hell-cup to the brim,
Its witchery, fiends, will have no charm for him.
Let loose your glowing wantons from their bowers,
He loves, he loves, and can defy their powers !
Wretch that I am, in *his* heart still I reign
Pure as when first we met, without a stain !
Though ruin'd — lost — my memory, like a charm
Left by the dead, still keeps his soul from harm.
Oh ! never let him know how deep the brow
He kiss'd at parting is dishonor'd now, —
Ne'er tell him how debased, how sunk, is she
Whom once he loved ! — once ! — *still* loves dotingly !
Thou laugh'st, tormentor, — what ! thou'lt brand my
　name ?

Do, do, — in vain; he'll not believe my shame.
He thinks me true, — that nought beneath God's
    sky
Could tempt or change me, and — so once thought I.
But this is past, — though worse than death my lot,
Than hell, 'tis nothing, while *he* knows it not.
Far off to some benighted land I'll fly,
Where sunbeam ne'er shall enter till I die;
Where none will ask the lost one whence she came,
But I may fade and fall without a name!
And thou — curst man or fiend, whate'er thou art,
Who found'st this burning plague-spot in my heart,
And spread'st it — oh, so quick! — through soul and
    frame,
With more than demon's art, till I became
A loathsome thing, all pestilence, all flame! —
If, when I'm gone — "

                              " Hold, fearless maniac, hold,
Nor tempt my rage! — by Heaven! not half so bold
The puny bird that dares, with teasing hum,
Within the crocodile's stretch'd jaws to come!
And so thou'lt fly, forsooth? — what! give up all
Thy chaste dominion in the Haram Hall,
Where now to Love and now to Alla given,
Half mistress and half saint, thou hang'st as even
As doth Medina's tomb, 'twixt hell and heaven!
Thou'lt fly? — as easily may reptiles run
The gaunt snake once hath fix'd his eyes upon;
As easily, when caught, the prey may be
Pluck'd from his loving folds, as thou from me.

No, no, 'tis fix'd, —
    let good or ill
    betide,
Thou'rt mine till death,
    till death Mokanna's
    bride !
Hast thou forgot thy oath? —"

            At this dread word,
The Maid, whose spirit his rude taunts
    had stirr'd
Through all its depths, and roused an anger
    there,
That burst and lighten'd even through her
    despair,
Shrunk back, as if a blight were in the breath
That spoke that word, and stagger'd, pale as
    death.

    "Yes, my sworn bride, let others seek in
        bowers
    Their bridal place, — the charnel vault was
        ours !
    Instead of scents and balms, for thee and me
    Rose the rich steams of sweet mortality ;
Gay, flickering death-lights shone while we were wed,
And, for our guests, a row of goodly dead
(Immortal spirits in their time, no doubt)
From reeking shrouds upon the rite look'd out !
That oath thou heard'st more lips than thine repeat ;
That cup, — thou shudderest, lady ; was it sweet ? —

That cup we pledged, the charnel's choicest wine, —
Hath bound thee, aye, body and soul all mine;
Bound thee by chains that, whether blest or curst,
No matter now, not hell itself shall burst !
Hence, woman, to the haram, and look gay,
Look wild, look — anything but sad; yet stay —
One moment more, — from what this night hath pass'd,
I see thou know'st me, know'st me *well* at last.
Ha ! ha ! and so, fond thing, thou thought'st all true,
And that I love mankind — I do, I do,
As victims, love them ; as the sea-dog doats
Upon the small sweet fry that round him floats,
Or as the Nile-bird loves the slime that gives
That rank and venomous food on which she lives!

   " And now thou seest my *soul's* angelic hue,
'Tis time these *features* were uncurtained too, —
This brow, whose light — oh, rare celestial light ! —
Hath been reserved to bless thy favour'd sight ;
These dazzling eyes, before whose shrouded might
Thou'st seen immortal Man kneel down and quake, —
Would that they *were* heaven's lightnings for his
      sake !
But turn and look ; then wonder, if thou wilt,
That I should hate, should take revenge, by guilt,
Upon the hand whose mischief or whose mirth
Sent me thus maim'd and monstrous upon earth,
And on that race who, though more vile they be
Than mowing apes, are demigods to me !
Here — judge if hell, with all its powers to damn,
Can add one curse to the foul thing I am ! " —

He raised his veil, — the Maid turn'd slowly round,
Look'd at him, shriek'd, and sunk upon the ground !

On their arrival, next night, at the place of encampment, they were surprised and delighted to find
the groves all around illuminated; some artists of
Yamtcheou having been sent on previously for the
purpose. On each side of the green alley which led
to the Royal Pavilion, artificial sceneries of bamboo
work were erected, representing arches, minarets, and
towers, from which hung thousands of silken lanterns,

painted by the most delicate pencils of Canton. Nothing could be more beautiful than the leaves of the
mango-trees and acacias, shining in the light of the
bamboo scenery, which shed a lustre around as soft as
that of the nights of Peristan.

Lalla Rookh, however, who was too much occupied
by the sad story of Zelica and her lover to give a
thought to anything else, except, perhaps, him who
related it, hurried on through this scene of splendour
to her pavilion, — greatly to the mortification of the
poor artists of Yamtcheou, — and was followed with
equal rapidity by the Great Chamberlain, cursing, as
he went, the ancient Mandarin whose parental anx-
iety in lighting up the shores of the lake where his
beloved daughter had wandered and been lost was
the origin of these fantastic Chinese illuminations.

Without a moment's delay, young Feramorz was
introduced ; and Fadladeen, who could never make up
his mind as to the merits of a poet till he knew the
religious sect to which he belonged, was about to ask
him whether he was a Shia or a Sooni, when Lalla
Rookh impatiently clapped her hands for silence, and
the youth, being seated upon the musnud near her,
proceeded : —

PREPARE thy soul, young Azim ! — thou hast braved
The bands of Greece, still mighty, though enslaved ;
Hast faced her phalanx, arm'd with all its fame,
Her Macedonian pikes and globes of flame ; —

All this hast fronted, with firm heart and brow :
But a more perilous trial waits thee now, —
Woman's bright eyes, a dazzling host of eyes
From every land where woman smiles or sighs ;
Of every hue, as Love may chance to raise
His black or azure banner in their blaze ;
And each sweet mode of warfare, from the flash
That lightens boldly through the shadowy lash,
To the sly, stealing splendours, almost hid,
Like swords half-sheathed, beneath the downcast lid.
Such, Azim, is the lovely, luminous host
Now led against thee ; and, let conquerors boast
Their fields of fame, he who in virtue arms
A young, warm spirit against beauty's charms,
Who feels her brightness, yet defies her thrall,
Is the best, bravest conqueror of them all.

Now, through the haram chambers, moving lights
And busy shapes proclaim the toilet's rites ;
From room to room the ready handmaids hie, —
Some skill'd to wreathe the turban tastefully,
Or hang the veil, in negligence of shade,
O'er the warm blushes of the youthful maid,
Who, if between the folds but *one* eye shone,
Like Seba's Queen could vanquish with that one ;
While some bring leaves of henna to imbue
The fingers' ends with a bright roseate hue,
So bright that in the mirror's depth they seem
Like tips of coral branches in the stream ;
And others mix the Kohol's jetty dye,
To give that long, dark languish to the eye,

Which makes the maids, whom kings are proud to
    cull
From fair Circassia's vales, so beautiful !

All is in motion : rings and plumes and pearls
Are shining everywhere ! Some younger girls
Are gone by moonlight to the garden beds,
To gather fresh, cool chaplets for their heads ; —
Gay creatures ! sweet, though mournful, 'tis to see
How each prefers a garland from that tree
Which brings to mind her childhood's innocent day,
And the dear fields and friendships far away.
The maid of India, blest again to hold
In her full lap the Champac's leaves of gold,
Thinks of the time when, by the Ganges' flood,
Her little playmates scatter'd many a bud
Upon her long black hair, with glossy gleam
Just dripping from the consecrated stream ;
While the young Arab, haunted by the smell
Of her own mountain flowers, as by a spell, —
The sweet Elcaya, and that courteous tree
Which bows to all who seek its canopy, —
Sees, call'd up round her by these magic scents,
The well, the camels, and her father's tents ;
Sighs for the home she left with little pain,
And wishes even its sorrows back again !

Meanwhile, through vast illuminated halls,
Silent and bright, where nothing but the falls
Of fragrant waters, gushing with cool sound
From many a jasper fount is heard around,

Young Azim roams be-
wilder'd, nor can
guess
What means this maze
of light and loneli-
ness.
Here the way leads, o'er
tesselated floors
Or mats of Cairo,
through long cor-
ridors,
Where, ranged
in casselets
and silver
urns,

Sweet wood of aloe or of sandal burns ;
And spicy rods, such as illume at night
The bowers of Tibet, send forth odorous light,
Like Peris' wands, when pointing out the road
For some pure spirit to its blest abode ! —
And here, at once, that glittering saloon
Bursts on his sight, boundless and bright as noon ;
Where, in the midst, reflecting back the rays
In broken rainbows, a fresh fountain plays
High as th' enamell'd cupola, which towers
All rich with arabesques of gold and flowers ;
And the mosaic floor beneath shines through
The sprinkling of that fountain's silvery dew,
Like the wet, glistening shells, of every dye,
That on the margin of the Red Sea lie.

Here too he traces the kind visitings
Of woman's love in those fair, living things
Of land and wave, whose fate — in bondage thrown
For their weak loveliness — is like her own !
On one side gleaming with a sudden grace
Through water, brilliant as the crystal vase
In which it undulates, small fishes shine,
Like golden ingots from a fairy mine ;
While, on the other, latticed lightly in
With odoriferous woods of Comorin,
Each brilliant bird that wings the air is seen, —
Gay, sparkling loories, such as gleam between
The crimson blossoms of the coral-tree
In the warm isles of India's sunny sea ;
Mecca's blue sacred pigeon, and the thrush

Of Hindostan, whose holy warblings gush,
At evening, from the tall pagoda's top;
Those golden birds that, in the spice time, drop
About the gardens, drunk with that sweet food
Whose scent hath lured them o'er the summer flood;
And those that under Araby's soft sun
Build their high nests of budding cinnamon; —
In short, all rare and beauteous things that fly
Through the pure element, here calmly lie
Sleeping in light, like the green birds that dwell
In Eden's radiant fields of asphodel!

So on, through scenes past all imagining, —
More like the luxuries of that impious king
Whom Death's dark angel, with his lightning torch,
Struck down and blasted even in pleasure's porch,
Than the pure dwelling of a prophet sent,
Arm'd with Heaven's sword, for man's enfranchise-
　　ment, —
Young Azim wander'd, looking sternly round,
His simple garb and war-boot's clanking sound
But ill according with the pomp and grace
And silent lull of that voluptuous place!

"Is this, then," thought the youth, "is this the
　　way
To free man's spirit from the deadening sway
Of worldly sloth, — to teach him, while he lives,
To know no bliss but that which virtue gives,
And when he dies, to leave his lofty name
A light, a landmark, on the cliffs of fame?

It was not so, land of the
generous thought
And daring deed! thy godlike sages
taught;
It was not thus, in bowers of wanton ease,
Thy Freedom nursed
her sacred energies;

Oh! not beneath
th' enfeebl-
ing, withering
glow

Of such dull luxury did those myrtles grow
With which she wreathed her sword, when she would
          dare
Immortal deeds ; but in the bracing air
Of toil, of temperance, of that high, rare,
Ethereal virtue, which alone can breathe
Life, health, and lustre into Freedom's wreath !
Who that surveys this span of earth we press,
This speck of life in time's great wilderness,
This narrow isthmus 'twixt two boundless seas, —
The past, the future, two eternities ! —
Would sully the bright spot or leave it bare,
When he might build him a proud temple there,
A name that long shall hallow all its space,
And be each purer soul's high resting-place !
But no ; it cannot be that one whom God
Has sent to break the wizard Falsehood's rod —
A prophet of the Truth, whose mission draws
Its rights from heaven — should thus profane his
          cause
With the world's vulgar pomps ; no, no, I see, —
He thinks me weak, — this glare of luxury
Is but to tempt, to try the eaglet gaze
Of my young soul ; — shine on, 'twill stand the blaze !"

    So thought the youth ; but even while he defied
This witching scene, he felt its witchery glide
Through every sense.   The perfume, breathing round,
Like a pervading spirit ; the still sound
Of falling waters, lulling as the song
Of Indian bees at sunset, when they throng

Around the fragrant Nilica, and deep
In its blue blossoms hum themselves to sleep!
And music, too, — dear music! that can touch
Beyond all else the soul that loves it much, —
Now heard far off, so far as but to seem
Like the faint, exquisite music of a dream; —
All was too much for him, too full of bliss;
The heart could nothing feel, that felt not this:
Soften'd he sunk upon a couch, and gave
His soul up to sweet thoughts, like wave on wave
Succeeding in smooth seas, when storms are laid;
He thought of Zelica, his own dear maid,
And of the time when, full of blissful sighs,
They sat and look'd into each other's eyes,
Silent and happy, as if God had given
Nought else worth looking at on this side heaven!

"O my loved mistress! whose spirit still
Is with me, round me, wander where I will,
It is for thee, for thee alone, I seek
The paths of glory, — to light up thy cheek
With warm approval, — in that gentle look
To read my praise, as in an angel's book,
And think all toils rewarded, when from thee
I gain a smile, worth immortality!
How shall I bear the moment, when restored
To that young heart where I alone am lord,
Though of such bliss unworthy, — since the best
Alone deserve to be the happiest! —
When from those lips, unbreathed upon for years,
I shall again kiss off the soul-felt tears,

And find those tears warm as when last they started,
Those sacred kisses pure as when we parted !
O my own life ! why should a single day,
A moment, keep me from those arms away ? "

While thus he thinks, still nearer on the breeze
Come those delicious, dream-like harmonies,
Each note of which but adds new, downy links
To the soft chain in which his spirit sinks.
He turns him toward the sound ; and far away
Through a long vista, sparkling with the play
Of countless lamps, — like the rich track which day
Leaves on the waters when he sinks from us,
So long the path, its light so tremulous, —
He sees a group of female forms advance :
Some chain'd together in the mazy dance
By fetters, forged in the green sunny bowers,
As they were captives to the King of Flowers ;
And some disporting round, unlink'd and free,
Who seem'd to mock their sisters' slavery,
And round and round them still, in wheeling flight,
Went, like gay moths about a lamp at night ;
While others waked, as gracefully along
Their feet kept time, the very soul of song
From psaltery, pipe, and lutes of heavenly thrill,
Or their own youthful voices, heavenlier still !
And now they come, now pass before his eye, —
Forms such as Nature moulds, when she would vie
With Fancy's pencil, and give birth to things
Lovely beyond its fairest picturings !
Awhile they dance before him, then divide

Breaking,
  like rosy
  clouds at
  even-tide
Around the rich
  pavilion of the sun,
Till silently dispers-
  ing, one by one,
Through many a path
  that from the chamber leads
To gardens, terraces, and moonlight meads,

Their distant laughter comes upon the wind,
And but one trembling nymph remains behind,
Beckoning them back in vain, for they are gone,
And she is left in all that light alone;
No veil to curtain o'er her beauteous brow,
In its young bashfulness more beauteous now,
But a light golden chain-work round her hair,
Such as the maids of Yezd and Shiraz wear,
From which, on either side, gracefully hung
A golden amulet, in th' Arab tongue
Engraven o'er with some immortal line
From holy writ, or bard scarce less divine;
While her left hand, as shrinkingly she stood,
Held a small lute of gold and sandal-wood,
Which once or twice she touch'd with hurried strain,
Then took her trembling fingers off again.
But when at length a timid glance she stole
At Azim, the sweet gravity of soul
She saw through all his features calm'd her fear,
And, like a half-tamed antelope, more near,
Though shrinking still, she came; then sat her down
Upon a musnud's edge, and, bolder grown,
In the pathetic mode of Isfahan
Touch'd a preluding strain, and thus began:

There's a bower of roses by Bendemeer's stream,
   And the nightingale sings round it all the day
     long.
In the time of my childhood 'twas like a sweet
     dream,
   To sit in the roses and hear the bird's song.

That bower and its music I never forget,
But oft when alone, in the
bloom of the year,
I think — is the nightin-
gale singing there
yet?
Are the roses still bright
by the calm
Bendemeer?

No, the roses
soon with-
er'd that
hung o'er
the wave;

But some blossoms were gather'd, while freshly they
   shone,
And a dew was distill'd from their flowers, that gave
   All the fragrance of summer, when summer was gone.

Thus memory draws from delight, ere it dies,
   An essence that breathes of it many a year;
Thus bright to my soul, as 'twas then to my eyes,
   Is that bower on the banks of the calm Bendemeer!

   "Poor maiden!" thought the youth, "if thou wert
   sent,
With thy soft lute and beauty's blandishment
To wake unholy wishes in this heart,
Or tempt its truth, thou little know'st the art;
For though thy lip should sweetly counsel wrong,
Those vestal eyes would disavow its song.
But thou hast breathed such purity, thy lay
Returns so fondly to youth's virtuous day,
And leads thy soul — if e'er it wander'd thence —
So gently back to its first innocence,
That I would sooner stop the unchain'd dove,
When swift returning to its home of love,
And round its snowy wing new fetters twine,
Than turn from virtue one pure wish of thine!"

   Scarce had this feeling pass'd when sparkling through
The gently open'd curtains of light blue
That veil'd the breezy casement, countless eyes,
Peeping like stars through the blue evening skies,
Look'd laughing in, as if to mock the pair
That sat so still and melancholy there.

And now the curtains fly apart, and in
From the cool air, 'mid showers of jessamine
Which those without fling after them in play,
Two lightsome maidens spring, lightsome as they
Who live in th' air on odours, and around
The bright saloon, scarce conscious of the ground,
Chase one another, in a varying dance
Of mirth and languor, coyness and advance,
Too eloquently like love's warm pursuit ;
While she who sung so gently to the lute
Her dream of home, steals timidly away,
Shrinking as violets do in summer's ray,
But takes with her from Azim's heart that sigh
We sometimes give to forms that pass us by
In the world's crowd, too lovely to remain,
Creatures of light we never see again !

Around the white necks of the nymphs who danced
Hung carcanets of orient gems, that glanced
More brilliant than the sea-glass glittering o'er
The hills of crystal on the Caspian shore ;
While from their long, dark tresses, in a fall
Of curls descending, bells as musical
As those that on the golden-shafted trees
Of Eden shake in the Eternal Breeze,
Rung round their steps, at every bound more sweet,
As 'twere th' ecstatic language of their feet !
At length the chase was o'er, and they stood wreathed
Within each other's arms ; while soft there breathed
Through the cool casement, mingled with the sighs
Of moonlight flowers, music that seem'd to rise

From some still
lake, so liquidly
it rose;
And, as it swell'd again at each
faint close,
The ear could track through all
that maze of chords
And young sweet voices, these
impassion'd words:

A Spirit there is, whose fragrant
sigh
Is burning now through earth
and air:
Where cheeks are blushing, the
Spirit is nigh;
Where lips are meeting, the
Spirit is there!

His breath is the soul of flowers
like these,

And his floating eyes — oh ! *they* resemble
Blue water-lilies, when the breeze
  Is making the stream around them tremble !

Hail to thee, hail to thee, kindling power !
  Spirit of Love ! Spirit of Bliss !
Thy holiest time is the moonlight hour,
  And there never was moonlight so sweet as this.

      By the fair and brave,
        Who blushing unite,
      Like the sun and wave,
        When they meet at night !

      By the tear that shows
        When passion is nigh,
      As the rain-drop flows
        From the heat of the sky !

      By the first love-beat
        Of the youthful heart,
      By the bliss to meet
        And the pain to part !

      By all that thou hast
        To mortals given,
      Which — oh ! could it last,
        This earth were heaven !

We call thee hither, entrancing Power !
  Spirit of Love ! Spirit of Bliss !
Thy holiest time is the moonlight hour,
  And there never was moonlight so sweet as this

Impatient of a scene
    whose luxuries stole,
Spite of himself, too deep
    into his soul,
And where, 'midst all that
    the young heart loves
    most,
Flowers, music, smiles, to
    yield was to be lost,
The youth hath started up,
    and turn'd away
From the light nymphs and
    their luxurious lay,
To muse upon the pictures
    that hung round, —
Bright images, that spoke
    without a sound,
And views, like vistas into
    fairy ground.
But here again new spells
    came o'er his sense :

All that the pencil's mute omnipotence
Could call up into life, of soft and fair,
Of fond and passionate, was glowing there;
Nor yet too warm, but touch'd with that fine art
Which paints of pleasure but the purer part;
Which knows e'en Beauty when half veil'd is best,
Like her own radiant planet of the west,
Whose orb when half retired looks loveliest!
There hung the history of the Genii-King,
Traced through each gay, voluptuous wandering
With her from Saba's bowers, in whose bright eyes
He read that to be blest is to be wise;
Here fond Zuleika wooes with open arms
The Hebrew boy, who flies from her young charms,
Yet, flying, turns to gaze, and, half undone,
Wishes that heaven and she could *both* be won!
And here Mohammed, born for love and guile,
Forgets the Koran in his Mary's smile;
Then beckons some kind angel from above
With a new text to consecrate their love!

With rapid step, yet pleased and lingering eye,
Did the youth pass these pictured stories by,
And hasten'd to a casement, where the light
Of the calm moon came in, and freshly bright
The fields without were seen, sleeping as still
As if no life remain'd in breeze or rill.
Here paused he, while the music, now less near,
Breathed with a holier language on his ear,
As though the distance and that heavenly ray
Through which the sounds came floating, took away

LR-F

All that had been too earthly in the lay.
Oh ! could he listen to such sounds unmoved,
And by that light, — nor dream of her he loved ?
Dream on, unconscious boy ! while yet thou may'st ;
'Tis the last bliss thy soul shall ever taste.
Clasp yet awhile her image to thy heart,
Ere all the light that made it dear depart.
Think of her smiles as when thou saw'st them last,
Clear, beautiful, by nought of earth o'ercast ;
Recall her tears, to thee at parting given,
Pure as they weep, *if* angels weep, in heaven !
Think in her own still bower she waits thee now,
With the same glow of heart and bloom of brow,
Yet shrined in solitude, — thine all, thine only,
Like the one star above thee, bright and lonely !
Oh that a dream so sweet, so long enjoy'd,
Should be so sadly, cruelly destroy'd !

The song is hush'd, the laughing nymphs are flown,
And he is left, musing of bliss, alone ; —
Alone ! no, not alone ; that heavy sigh,
That sob of grief, which broke from some one nigh, —
Whose could it be ? — alas ! is misery found
Here, even here, on this enchanted ground ?
He turns, and sees a female form, close veil'd,
Leaning as if both heart and strength had fail'd,
Against a pillar near, — not glittering o'er
With gems and wreaths, such as the others wore,
But in that deep blue, melancholy dress
Bokhara's maidens wear, in mindfulness
Of friends or kindred, dead or far away ; —

And such as Zelica had on
    that day
He left her, — when, with
    heart too full to speak,
He took away her last warm
    tears upon his cheek.

  A strong emotion stirs
    within him, — more
Than mere compassion ever
    waked before;
Unconsciously
    he opes
    his arms,
    while she

Springs forward, as with life's last energy,
But, swooning in that one convulsive bound,
Sinks, ere she reaches his arms, upon the ground.
Her veil falls off, her faint hands clasp his knees,
'Tis she herself! — 'tis Zelica he sees!
But, ah, so pale, so changed, none but a lover
Could in that wreck of beauty's shrine discover
The once adored divinity! even he
Stood for some moments mute, and doubtingly
Put back the ringlets from her brow, and gazed
Upon those lids, where once such lustre blazed,
Ere he could think she was *indeed* his own,
Own darling maid, whom he so long had known
In joy and sorrow, beautiful in both;
Who, e'en when grief was heaviest, — when loath
He left her for the wars, — in that worst hour
Sat in her sorrow like the sweet night flower,
When darkness brings its weeping glories out,
And spreads its sighs like frankincense about!

" Look up, my Zelica, — one moment show
Those gentle eyes to me, that I may know
Thy life, thy loveliness, is not all gone,
But *there*, at least, shines as it ever shone.
Come, look upon thy Azim, — one dear glance,
Like those of old, were heaven! whatever chance
Hath brought thee here, oh, 'twas a blessed one!
There — my sweet lids — they move, — that kiss hath run
Like the first shoot of life, through every vein,
And now I clasp her, mine, all mine again!
Oh the delight — now, in this very hour,

When, had the whole rich world been in my power,
I should have singled out thee, only thee,
From the whole world's collected treasury, —

To have thee here, — to hang thus fondly o'er
My own best, purest Zelica once more!"

    It was indeed the touch of those fond lips
Upon her eyes that chased their short eclipse,

And gradual, as the snow at heaven's breath
Melts off and shows the azure flowers beneath,
Her lids unclosed, and the bright eyes were seen,
Gazing on his, — not, as they late had been,
Quick, restless, wild, but mournfully serene ;
As if to lie, e'en for that trancèd minute,
So near his heart, had consolation in it,
And thus to wake in his beloved caress
Took from her soul one half its wretchedness.
But when she heard him call her good and pure,
Oh, 'twas too much, — too dreadful to endure !
Shuddering, she broke away from his embrace,
And, hiding with both hands her guilty face,
Said, in a tone whose anguish would have riven
A heart of very marble, " Pure ? — O Heaven ! "

That tone, — those looks so changed, — the wither-
        ing blight
That sin and sorrow leave where'er they light, —
The dead despondency of those sunk eyes,
Where once, had he thus met her by surprise,
He would have seen himself, too happy boy,
Reflected in a thousand lights of joy, —
And then the place, that bright unholy place,
Where vice lay hid beneath each winning grace
And charm of luxury, as the viper weaves
Its wily covering of sweet balsam-leaves, —
All struck upon his heart, sudden and cold
As death itself ; it needs not to be told, —
No, no, — he sees it all, plain as the brand
Of burning shame can mark, — whate'er the hand

That could from heaven and him such brightness
    sever,
'Tis done, — to heaven and him she's lost for ever!
It was a dreadful moment; not the tears,
The lingering, lasting misery of years,
Could match that minute's anguish, — all the worst
Of sorrow's elements in that dark burst
Broke o'er his soul, and with one crash of fate
Laid the whole hopes of his life desolate!

    "Oh! curse me not," she cried, as wild he toss'd
His desperate hand toward heaven — "though I am
    lost,
Think not that guilt, that falsehood, made me fall;
No, no, — 'twas grief, 'twas madness, did it all!
Nay, doubt me not; though all thy love hath
    ceased, —
I know it hath, — yet, yet believe, at least,
That every spark of reason's light must be
Quench'd in this brain ere I could stray from thee!
They told me thou wert dead, — why, Azim, why
Did we not, both of us, that instant die
When we were parted? — oh! couldst thou but know
With what a deep devotedness of woe
I wept thy absence, — o'er and o'er again
Thinking of thee, still thee, till thought grew pain,
And memory, like a drop that, night and day,
Falls cold and ceaseless, wore my heart away, —
Didst thou but know how pale I sat at home,
My eyes still turn'd the way thou wert to come,
And, all the long, long night of hope and fear,

Thy voice and step still sounding in my ear, —
O God! thou wouldst not wonder that, at last,
When every hope was all at once o'ercast,
When I heard frightful voices round me say
Azim is dead! — this wretched brain gave way,
And I became a wreck, at random driven,
Without one glimpse of reason or of heaven, —
All wild, — and even this quenchless love within
Turn'd to foul fires to light me into sin!
Thou pitiest me, — I knew thou wouldst; that sky
Hath nought beneath it half so lorn as I.
The fiend, who lured me hither, — hist! come near,
Or thou too, *thou* art lost, if he should hear, —
Told me such things — oh! with such devilish art
As would have ruin'd even a holier heart —
Of thee, and of that ever-radiant sphere,

Where bless'd at length, if I but served *him* here,
I should for ever live in thy dear sight,
And drink from those pure eyes eternal light!
Think, think how lost, how madden'd, I must be,
To hope that guilt could lead to God or thee!
Thou weep'st for me, — do weep — oh that I durst
Kiss off that tear! but, no, — these lips are curst,
They must not touch thee; — one divine caress,
One blessed moment of forgetfulness,
I've had within those arms, and *that* shall lie
Shrined in my soul's deep memory till I die!
The last of joy's last relics here below,
The one sweet drop, in all this waste of woe,
My heart has treasured from affection's spring,
To soothe and cool its deadly withering!
But thou — yes, thou must go — for ever go;
This place is not for thee — for thee! oh, no!
Did I but tell thee half, thy tortured brain
Would burn like mine, and mine go wild again!
Enough that Guilt reigns here, — that hearts once
    good,
Now tainted, chill'd, and broken, are his food;
Enough that we are parted, — that there rolls
A flood of headlong fate between our souls,
Whose darkness severs me as wide from thee
As hell from heaven, to all eternity!"—

"Zelica! Zelica!" the youth exclaim'd,
In all the tortures of a mind inflamed
Almost to madness, "by that sacred heaven,
Where yet, if prayers can move, thou'lt be forgiven

As thou art here — here in this writhing heart,
All sinful, wild, and ruin'd as thou art!
By the remembrance of our once pure love,
Which, like a churchyard light, still burns above
The grave of our lost souls, — which guilt in thee
Cannot extinguish, nor despair in me! —
I do conjure, implore thee to fly hence;
If thou hast yet one spark of innocence,
Fly with me from this place — "

                " With thee! oh, bliss,
'Tis worth whole years of torment to hear this.
What! take the lost one with thee? — let her rove
By thy dear side, as in those days of love,
When we were both so happy, both so pure —
Too heavenly dream! if there's on earth a cure
For the sunk heart, 'tis this, — day after day
To be the blest companion of thy way;
To hear thy angel eloquence; to see
Those virtuous eyes for ever turn'd on me,
And in their light re-chasten'd silently, —
Like the stain'd web that whitens in the sun,
Grow pure by being purely shone upon.
And thou wilt pray for me, — I know thou wilt:
At the dim vesper hour, when thoughts of guilt
Come heaviest o'er the heart, thou'lt lift thine eyes,
Full of sweet tears, into the darkening skies,
And plead for me with Heaven, till I can dare
To fix my own weak, sinful glances there;
Till the good angels, when they see me cling
For ever near thee, pale and sorrowing,
Shall for thy sake pronounce my soul forgiven,

And bid thee take thy weeping slave to heaven :
Oh, yes, I'll fly with thee — "
                              Scarce had she said
These breathless words, when a voice deep and dread
As that of Monker, waking up the dead
From their first sleep, — so startling 'twas to both, —
Rung through the casement near, "Thy oath! thy
      oath!"
O Heaven, the ghastliness of that Maid's look! —
"'Tis he," faintly she cried, while terror shook
Her inmost core, nor durst she lift her eyes,
Though through the casement now nought but the
      skies
And moonlight fields were seen, calm as before, —
"'Tis he, and I am his — all, all is o'er —
Go — fly this instant, or thou'rt ruin'd too —
My oath, my oath, O God ! 'tis all too true,
True as the worm in this cold heart it is —
I am Mokanna's bride — his, Azim, his —
The dead stood round us, while I spoke that vow,
Their blue lips echoed it — I hear them now !
Their eyes glared on me while I pledged that bowl ;
'Twas burning blood — I feel it in my soul !
And the Veiled Bridegroom — hist ! I've seen to-night
What angels know not of, — so foul a sight,
So horrible — oh ! never mayst thou see
What *there* lies hid from all but hell and me !
But I must hence — off, off — I am not thine,
Nor Heaven's, nor Love's, nor nought that is divine —
Hold me not — ha ! — think'st thou the fiends that
      sever

Hearts, cannot sunder
  hands? — thus, then
    — for ever!"

  With all that strength which mad-
    ness lends the weak,
She flung away his arms; and with a
  shriek,
Whose sound, though he should
  linger out more years

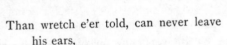

Than wretch e'er told, can never leave
  his ears,
Flew up through that long avenue of
  light,
Fleetly as some dark, ominous bird of
  night
Across the sun, and soon was out of
  sight!

LALLA ROOKH could think of nothing all day but
the misery of these two young lovers. Her gaiety
was gone, and she looked pensively even upon Fadladeen. She felt too, without knowing why, a sort of
uneasy pleasure in imagining that Azim must have
been just such a youth as Feramorz; just as worthy to
enjoy all the blessings, without any of the pangs, of
that illusive passion, which too often, like the sunny
apples of Istakhar, is all sweetness on one side, and
all bitterness on the other.

As they passed along a sequestered river after sunset, they saw a young Hindoo girl upon the bank,
whose employment seemed to them so strange that
they stopped their palankeens to observe her. She
had lighted a small lamp, filled with oil of cocoa, and
placing it in an earthen dish, adorned with a wreath
of flowers, had committed it with a trembling hand
to the stream, and was now anxiously watching its
progress down the current, heedless of the gay
cavalcade which had drawn up beside her. Lalla
Rookh was all curiosity; when one of her attendants, who had lived upon the banks of the Ganges
(where this ceremony is so frequent that often,
in the dusk of the evening, the river is seen glittering all over with lights, like the Oton-tala, or Sea
of Stars), informed the Princess that it was the usual
way in which the friends of those who had gone on
dangerous voyages offered up vows for their safe
return. If the lamp sunk immediately, the omen
was disastrous; but if it went shining down the
stream, and continued to burn until entirely out of

sight, the return of the beloved object was con-
sidered as certain.

Lalla Rookh, as they moved on, more than once
looked back, to observe how the young Hindoo's lamp
proceeded, and while she saw with pleasure that it
was still unextinguished, she could not help fearing
that all the hopes of this life were no better than that
feeble light upon the river. The remainder of the
journey was passed in silence. She now, for the first
time, felt that shade of melancholy which comes over
the youthful maiden's heart, as sweet and transient as
her own breath upon a mirror; nor was it till she
heard the lute of Feramorz, touched lightly at the door
of her pavilion, that she waked from the reverie in
which she had been wandering. Instantly her eyes
were lighted up with pleasure, and, after a few unheard
remarks from Fadladeen upon the indecorum of a
poet seating himself in presence of a princess, everything was arranged as on the preceding evening, and
all listened with eagerness, while the story was thus
continued : —

WHOSE are the gilded tents that crowd the way,
Where all was waste and silent yesterday?
This City of War which, in a few short hours,
Hath sprung up here, as if the magic powers
Of him who, in the twinkling of a star,
Built the high pillar'd walls of Chilminar,
Had conjured up, far as the eye can see,
This world of tents and domes and sun-bright
    armory ! —

Princely pavilions, screen'd by many a fold
Of crimson cloth, and topp'd with balls of gold;
Steeds, with their housings of rich silver spun,
Their chains and poitrels glittering in the sun;
And camels, tufted o'er with Yemen's shells,
Shaking in every breeze their light-toned bells!

But yester-eve, so motionless around,
So mute was this wide plain, that not a sound
But the far torrent, or the locust-bird
Hunting among the thickets, could be heard;
Yet, hark! what discords now, of every kind,
Shouts, laughs, and screams, are revelling in the wind!
The neigh of cavalry; the tinkling throngs
Of laden camels and their drivers' songs;
Ringing of arms, and flapping in the breeze
Of streamers from ten thousand canopies;
War-music, bursting out from time to time
With gong and tymbalon's tremendous chime;
Or, in the pause, when harsher sounds are mute,
The mellow breathings of some horn or flute,
That far off, broken by the eagle note
Of th' Abyssinian trumpet, swell and float!

Who leads this mighty army? — ask ye " who?"
And mark ye not those banners of dark hue,
The Night and Shadow, over yonder tent! —
It is the Caliph's glorious armament.
Roused in his palace by the dread alarms,
That hourly came, of the false Prophet's arms,
And of his host of infidels, who hurl'd

Defiance fierce at Islam and the world:
Though worn with Grecian warfare, and behind
The veils of his bright palace calm reclined,
Yet brook'd he not such blasphemy should stain,

Thus unrevenged, the evening of his reign,
But, having sworn upon the Holy Grave
To conquer or to perish, once more gave
His shadowy banners proudly to the breeze,
And with an army nursed in victories,
Here stands to crush the rebels that o'errun
His blest and beauteous province of the sun.

Ne'er did the march of Mahadi display
Such pomp before ; — not e'en when on his way
To Mecca's temple, when both land and sea
Were spoil'd to feed the pilgrim's luxury ;
When round him, 'mid the burning sands, he saw
Fruits of the north in icy freshness thaw,
And cool'd his thirsty lip, beneath the glow
Of Mecca's sun, with urns of Persian snow ; —
Nor e'er did armament more grand than that
Pour from the kingdoms of the Caliphat.
First, in the van, the People of the Rock,
On their light mountain steeds, of royal stock ;
Then chieftains of Damascus, proud to see
The flashing of their swords' rich marquetry ; —
Men from the regions near the Volga's mouth,
Mix'd with the rude, black archers of the south ;
And Indian lancers, in white-turban'd ranks
From the far Sinde, or Attock's sacred banks,
With dusky legions from the Land of Myrrh,
And many a mace-arm'd Moor and Mid-Sea islander.

Nor less in number, though more new and rude
In warfare's school, was the vast multitude
That, fired by zeal, or by oppression wrong'd,
Round the white standard of th' impostor throng'd.
Beside his thousands of believers, — blind,
Burning and headlong as the Samiel wind, —
Many who felt, and more who fear'd to feel,
The bloody Islamite's converting steel,
Flock'd to his banner ; — chiefs of th' Uzbek race,
Waving their heron crests with martial grace ;

Turkomans, countless as their flocks, led forth
From th' aromatic pastures of the north;
Wild warriors of the turquoise hills, — and those
Who dwell beyond the everlasting snows
Of Hindoo Kosh, in stormy freedom bred,
Their fort the rock, their camp the torrent's bed.
But none, of all who own'd the Chief's command,
Rush'd to that battle-field with bolder hand
Or sterner hate than Iran's outlaw'd men,
Her Worshippers of Fire, — all panting then
For vengeance on th' accursed Saracen;
Vengeance at last for their dear country spurn'd,
Her throne usurp'd, and her bright shrines o'erturn'd.
From Yezd's eternal Mansion of the Fire,
Where aged saints in dreams of heaven expire;
From Badku, and those fountains of blue flame
That burn into the Caspian, — fierce they came;
Careless for what or whom the blow was sped,
So vengeance triumph'd, and their tyrants bled!

Such was the wild and miscellaneous host
That high in air their motley banners toss'd
Around the Prophet-Chief, — all eyes still bent
Upon that glittering Veil, where'er it went,
That beacon through the battle's stormy flood,
That rainbow of the field, whose showers were blood!

Twice hath the sun upon their conflict set,
And ris'n again, and found them grappling yet;
While streams of carnage, in his noontide blaze,
Smoke up to heaven, — hot as that crimson haze,

By which the prostrate caravan
    is awed,
  In the red Desert, when the wind's abroad!
" On, Swords of God!" the panting Caliph
    calls, —
" Thrones for the living, — heaven for him who
    falls!"
" On, brave avengers, on," Mokanna cries,

" And Eblis blast the recreant slave that flies ! "
Now comes the brunt, the crisis of the day —
They clash — they strive — the Caliph's troops give
      way !
Mokanna's self plucks the black Banner down,

And now the Orient World's imperial crown
Is just within his grasp — when, hark, that shout!
Some hand hath check'd the flying Moslem's rout
And now they turn — they rally — at their head
A warrior (like those angel youths, who led,
In glorious panoply of heaven's own mail,
The Champions of the Faith through Beder's vale),
Bold as if gifted with ten thousand lives,
Turns on the fierce pursuers' blades, and drives
At once the multitudinous torrent back,
While hope and courage kindle in his track,
And, at each step, his bloody falchion makes
Terrible vistas through which victory breaks!
In vain Mokanna, 'midst the general flight,
Stands, like the red moon, on some stormy night,
Among the fugitive clouds that, hurrying by,
Leave only her unshaken in the sky! —
In vain he yells his desperate curses out,
Deals death promiscuously to all about,
To foes that charge and coward friends that fly,
And seems of *all* the great Arch-enemy!
The panic spreads — "a miracle!" throughout
The Moslem ranks, "a miracle!" they shout,
All gazing on that youth, whose coming seems
A light, a glory, such as breaks in dreams;
And every sword, true as o'er billows dim
The needle tracks the loadstar, following him!

Right tow'rds Mokanna now he cleaves his path,
Impatient cleaves, as though the bolt of wrath
He bears from heaven withheld its awful burst

From weaker heads, and souls but half-way curst,
To break o'er him, the mightiest and the worst!
But vain his speed — though, in that hour of blood,
Had all God's seraphs round Mokanna stood,
With swords of fire, ready like fate to fall,
Mokanna's soul would have defied them all; —
Yet now the rush of fugitives, too strong
For human force, hurries even *him* along;
In vain he struggles 'mid the wedged array
Of flying thousands, — he is borne away;
And the sole joy his baffled spirit knows
In this forced flight is — murdering as he goes!
As a grim tiger, whom the torrent's might
Surprises in some parch'd ravine at night,
Turns, even in drowning, on the wretched flocks
Swept with him in that snow-flood from the rocks,
And, to the last, devouring on his way,
Bloodies the stream he hath not power to stay!

"Alla illa Alla!" the glad shout renew —
"Alla Akbar!" — the Caliph's in Merou.
Hang out your gilded tapestry in the streets,
And light your shrines and chant your ziraleets;
The Swords of God have triumph'd, — on his throne
Your Caliph sits, and the Veil'd Chief hath flown.
Who does not envy that young warrior now,
To whom the Lord of Islam bends his brow,
In all the graceful gratitude of power,
For his throne's safety in that perilous hour?
Who doth not wonder, when, amidst th' acclaim
Of thousands, heralding to heaven his name, —

'Mid all those holier harmonies of fame,
Which sound along the path of virtuous souls,
Like music round a planet as it rolls ! —
He turns away, coldly, as if some gloom
Hung o'er his heart no triumphs can illume, —
Some sightless grief, upon whose blasted gaze
Though glory's light may play, in vain it plays !
Yes, wretched Azim ! thine is such a grief,
Beyond all hope, all terror, all relief ;
A dark, cold calm, which nothing now can break,
Or warm, or brighten, — like that Syrian lake
Upon whose surface morn and summer shed
Their smiles in vain, for all beneath is dead ! —
Hearts there have been, o'er which this weight of woe
Came, by long use of suffering, tame and slow ;
But thine, lost youth ! was sudden, — over thee
It broke at once, when all seem'd ecstasy ;
When Hope look'd up, and saw the gloomy past
Melt into splendour, and Bliss dawn at last, —
'Twas then, even then, o'er joys so freshly blown,
This mortal blight of misery came down ;
Even then the full, warm gushings of thy heart
Were check'd, — like fount-drops, frozen as they start !
And there, like them, cold, sunless relics hang,
Each fix'd and chill'd into a lasting pang !

One sole desire, one passion now remains,
To keep life's fever still within his veins, —
Vengeance ! — dire vengeance on the wretch who cast
O'er him and all he loved that ruinous blast.
For this, when rumours reach'd him in his flight

Far, far away, after that fatal
    night, —
Rumours of armies, throng-
    ing to th' attack

Of the Veil'd Chief, — for this he wing'd him back,
Fleet as the vulture speeds to flags unfurl'd,
And, when all hope seem'd desperate, wildly hurl'd
Himself into the scale, and saved a world !
For this he still lives on, careless of all
The wreaths that glory on his path lets fall;
For this alone exists, — like lightning fire
To speed one bolt of vengeance, and expire !

But safe as yet that Spirit of Evil lives;
With a small band of desperate fugitives,
The last sole stubborn fragment left unriven
Of the proud host that late stood fronting heaven,
He gain'd Merou, — breathed a short curse of blood
O'er his lost throne, — then pass'd the Jihon's flood,
And gathering all whose madness of belief
Still saw a saviour in their down-fallen Chief,
Raised the white banner within Neksheb's gates,
And there, untamed, th' approaching conqueror waits.

Of all his haram, all that busy hive,
With music and with sweets sparkling alive,
He took but one, the partner of his flight, —
One, not for love, not for her beauty's light —
No, Zelica stood withering 'midst the gay,
Wan as the blossom that fell yesterday
From th' Alma tree and dies, while overhead
To-day's young flower is springing in its stead !
Oh, not for love, — the deepest damn'd must be
Touch'd with heaven's glory, ere such fiends as he
Can feel one glimpse of love's divinity !

But no, she is his victim; *there* lie all
Her charms for him, — charms that can never pall,
As long as hell within his heart can stir,
Or one faint trace of heaven is left in her.
To work an angel's ruin, — to behold
As white a page as virtue e'er unroll'd
Blacken, beneath his touch, into a scroll
Of damning sins, seal'd with a burning soul, —
This is his triumph ; this the joy accursed,
That ranks him among demons all but first!
This gives the victim, that before him lies
Blighted and lost, a glory in his eyes,
A light like that with which hell-fire illumes
The ghastly, writhing wretch whom it consumes !

But other tasks now wait him, — tasks that need
All the deep daringness of thought and deed
With which the Dives have gifted him ; for mark,
Over yon plains, which night had else made dark,
Those lanterns, countless as the wingèd lights
That spangle India's fields on showery nights,
Far as their formidable gleams they shed,
The mighty tents of the beleaguerer spread,
Glimmering along th' horizon's dusky line,
And thence in nearer circles, till they shine
Among the founts and groves, o'er which the town
In all its arm'd magnificence looks down.
Yet, fearless, from his lofty battlements
Mokanna views that multitude of tents ;
Nay, smiles to think that, though entoil'd, beset,
Not less than myriads dare to front him yet, —

That friendless, throneless, he thus stands at bay,
Even thus a match for myriads such as they !
" Oh for a sweep of that dark Angel's wing,
Who brush'd the thousands of th' Assyrian king
To darkness in a moment, that I might
People hell's chambers with yon host to-night !
But come what may, let who will grasp the throne,
Caliph or prophet, Man alike shall groan ;
Let who will torture him, priest, caliph, king, —
Alike this loathsome world of his shall ring
With victims' shrieks and howlings of the slave, —
Sounds that shall glad me even within my grave ! "
Thus to himself — but to the scanty train,
Still left around him, a far different strain :
" Glorious defenders of the sacred crown
I bear from heaven, whose light nor blood shall drown
Nor shadow of earth eclipse ; before whose gems
The paly pomp of this world's diadems,
The crown of Gerashid, the pillar'd throne
Of Parviz, and the heron crest that shone,
Magnificent, o'er Ali's beauteous eyes,
Fade like the stars when morn is in the skies !
Warriors, rejoice, — the port, to which we've pass'd
O'er destiny's dark wave, beams out at last :
Victory's our own, — 'tis written in that book
Upon whose leaves none but the angels look,
That Islam's sceptre shall beneath the power
Of her great foe fall broken in that hour
When the moon's mighty orb before all eyes
From Neksheb's Holy Well portentously shall rise !
Now turn and see ! — "

They turn'd, and, as he spoke,
A sudden splendour all around
      them broke ;
And they beheld an orb, ample
      and bright,
Rise from the Holy Well, and
      cast its light
Round the rich city and the plain for miles,
Flinging such radiance o'er the gilded tiles

Of many a dome and fair-roof'd imaret
As autumn suns shed round them when they set!
Instant from all who saw th' illusive sign,
A murmur broke, — " Miraculous ! divine ! "
The Gheber bow'd, thinking his idol star
Had waked, and burst impatient through the bar
Of midnight to inflame him to the war !
While he of Moussa's creed saw in that ray
The glorious light which, in his freedom's day,
Had rested on the Ark, and now again
Shone out to bless the breaking of his chain !

" To victory ! " is at once the cry of all —
Nor stands Mokanna loitering at that call ;
But instant the huge gates are flung aside,
And forth, like a diminutive mountain-tide
Into the boundless sea, they speed their course
Right on into the Moslem's mighty force.
The watchmen of the camp — who, in their rounds,
Had paused, and even forgot the punctual sounds
Of the small drum with which they count the night,
To gaze upon that supernatural light —
Now sink beneath an unexpected arm,
And in a death-groan give their last alarm.
" On for the lamps that light yon lofty screen,
Nor blunt your blades with massacre so mean ;
There rests the Caliph — speed — one lucky lance
May now achieve mankind's deliverance ! "
Desperate the die, — such as they only cast,
Who venture for a world, and stake their last.
But Fate's no longer with him, — blade for blade

Springs up to meet them through the glimmering
    shade;
And, as the clash is heard, new legions soon
Pour to the spot, — like bees of Kauzeroon
To the shrill timbrel's summons, — till at length
The mighty camp swarms out in all its strength,
And back to Neksheb's gates, covering the plain
With random slaughter, drives the adventurous train;
Among the last of whom the Silver Veil
Is seen glittering at times, like the white sail
Of some toss'd vessel, on a stormy night,
Catching the tempest's momentary light.

And hath not *this* brought the proud spirit low,
Nor dash'd his brow, nor check'd his daring? No!
Though half the wretches whom at night he led
To thrones and victory, lie disgraced and dead,
Yet morning hears him, with unshrinking crest,
Still vaunt of thrones and victory to the rest;
And they believe him! — oh! the lover may
Distrust that look that steals his soul away;
The babe may cease to think that it can play
With heaven's rainbow; alchemists may doubt
The shining gold their crucible gives out; —
But Faith, fanatic Faith, once wedded fast
To some dear falsehood, hugs it to the last.

And well th' impostor knew all lures and arts
That Lucifer e'er taught to tangle hearts;
Nor, 'mid these last bold workings of his plot
Against men's souls, is Zelica forgot.

Ill-fated Zelica! had reason been
Awake, through half the horrors thou hast seen,
Thou never couldst have borne it, — death had come
At once, and taken thy wrung spirit home.
But 'twas not so, — a torpor, a suspense
Of thought, almost of life, came o'er th' intense
And passionate struggles of that fearful night,
When her last hope of peace and heaven took flight;
And though, at times, a gleam of frenzy broke, —
As through some dull volcano's veil of smoke
Ominous flashings now and then will start,
Which show the fire still busy at its heart;
Yet was she mostly wrapp'd in sullen gloom, —
Not such as Azim's, brooding o'er its doom,
And calm without, as is the brow of death,
While busy worms are gnawing underneath! —
But in a blank and pulseless torpor, free
From thought of pain, a seal'd up apathy,
Which left her oft, with scarce one living thrill,
The cold, pale victim of her torturer's will.

Again, as in Merou, he had her deck'd
Gorgeously out, the Priestess of the sect;
And led her glittering forth before the eyes
Of his rude train, as to a sacrifice;
Pallid as she, the young, devoted Bride
Of the fierce Nile, when, deck'd in all the pride
Of nuptial pomp, she sinks into his tide!
And while the wretched maid hung down her head,
And stood, as one just risen from the dead,
Amid that gazing crowd, the fiend would tell

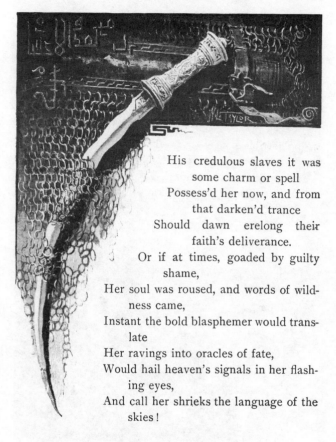

His credulous slaves it was
some charm or spell
Possess'd her now, and from
that darken'd trance
Should dawn erelong their
faith's deliverance.
Or if at times, goaded by guilty
shame,
Her soul was roused, and words of wildness came,
Instant the bold blasphemer would trans-
late
Her ravings into oracles of fate,
Would hail heaven's signals in her flashing eyes,
And call her shrieks the language of the
skies!

But vain at length his arts, — despair is seen
Gathering around; and famine comes to glean
All that the sword had left unreap'd; — in vain
At morn and eve across the northern plain

LR-H

He looks impatient for the promised
    spears
Of the wild hordes and Tartar moun-
    taineers ;
They come not, — while his fierce
    beleaguerers pour
Engines of havoc in, unknown
    before,
And horrible as new ; — javelins
    that fly
Enwreathed with smoky
    flames through the dark
    sky ;
And red-hot globes that,
    opening as they
    mount,
Discharge, as from a
    kindled naphtha
    fount,
Showers of con-
    suming
    fire o'er
    all be-
    low, —

Looking, as through th' illumined night they go,
Like those wild birds that by the Magians oft,
At festivals of fire, were sent aloft
Into the air, with blazing fagots tied
To their huge wings, scattering combustion wide!
All night the groans of wretches who expire
In agony beneath these darts of fire,
Ring through the city; while, descending o'er
Its shrines and domes and streets of sycamore, —
Its lone bazars, with their bright cloths of gold,
Since the last peaceful pageant left unroll'd, —
Its beauteous marble baths, whose idle jets
Now gush with blood, — and its tall minarets,
That late have stood up in the evening glare
Of the red sun, unhallow'd by a prayer, —
O'er each, in turn, the dreadful flame-bolts fall,
And death and conflagration throughout all
The desolate city hold high festival!

 Mokanna sees the world is his no more,
One sting at parting, and his grasp is o'er.
"What! drooping now?" — thus with unblushing
  cheek,
He hails the few who yet can hear him speak,
Of all those famish'd slaves around him lying,
And by the light of blazing temples'dying, —
"What! drooping now? — now, when at length we press
Home o'er the very threshold of success;
When Alla from our ranks hath thinn'd away
Those grosser branches, that kept out his ray
Of favour from us, and we stand at length

Heirs of his light and children of his strength, —
The chosen few, who shall survive the fall
Of kings and thrones, triumphant over all!
Have you then lost, weak murmurers as you are,
All faith in him who was your Light, your Star?
Have you forgot the eyes of glory hid
Beneath this Veil, the flashing of whose lid
Could, like a sun-stroke of the desert, wither
Millions of such as yonder chief brings hither?
Long have its lightnings slept, — too long, — but now,
All earth shall feel th' unveiling of this brow!
To-night, — yes, sainted men! this very night,
I bid you all to a fair festal rite,
Where, having deep refresh'd each weary limb
With viands, such as feast heaven's cherubim,
And kindled up your souls, now sunk and dim,
With that pure wine the Dark-eyed Maids above
Keep, seal'd with precious musk, for those they love,
I will myself uncurtain in your sight
The wonders of this brow's ineffable light;
Then lead you forth, and with a wink disperse
Yon myriads, howling through the universe!"

Eager they listen, while each accent darts
New life into their chill'd and hope-sick hearts, —
Such treacherous life as the cool draught supplies
To him upon the stake, who drinks and dies!
Wildly they point their lances to the light
Of the fast-sinking sun, and shout "To-night!" —
"To-night," their Chief re-echoes, in a voice
Of fiend-like mockery that bids hell rejoice!

Deluded victims — never hath this earth
Seen mourning half so mournful as their mirth!
Here, to the few whose iron frames had stood
This racking waste of famine and of blood,
Faint, dying wretches clung, from whom the shout
Of triumph like a maniac's laugh broke out;
There, others, lighted by the smouldering fire,
Danced, like wan ghosts about a funeral pyre,
Among the dead and dying, strew'd around;
While some pale wretch look'd on, and from his
        wound
Plucking the fiery dart by which he bled,
In ghastly transport waved it o'er his head!

'Twas more than midnight now, — a fearful pause
Had follow'd the long shout, the wild applause,
That lately from those Royal Gardens burst,
Where the Veil'd Demon held his feast accurst,
When Zelica — alas, poor ruin'd heart,
In every horror doom'd to bear its part! —
Was bidden to the banquet by a slave,
Who, while his quivering lip the summons gave,
Grew black, as though the shadows of the grave
Compass'd him round, and, ere he could repeat
His message through, fell lifeless at her feet!
Shuddering she went: a soul-felt pang of fear,
A presage, that her own dark doom was near,
Roused every feeling, and brought reason back
Once more, to writhe her last upon the rack.
All round seem'd tranquil, — even the foe had ceased,
As if aware of that demoniac feast,

His fiery bolts ; and though the heavens look'd red,
'Twas but some distant conflagration's spread.
But, hark ! — she stops — she listens — dreadful tone !
'Tis her Tormentor's laugh ; and now, a groan,
A long death-groan, comes with it, — can this be
The place of mirth, the bower of revelry ?

She enters, — holy
Alla, what a sight
Was there before
her ! By the
glimmering light
Of the pale dawn,
mix'd with the
flare of brands
That round lay
burning, dropp'd
from lifeless
hands,

She saw the board, in splendid mockery spread,
Rich censers breathing, — garlands
        overhead, —
The urns, the cups, from which
        they late had quaff'd,

All gold and gems, but — what had been the draught ?
Oh ! who need ask that saw those livid guests,
With their swollen heads sunk blackening on their
        breasts,
Or looking pale to heaven with glassy glare
As if they sought, but saw, no mercy there ;
As if they felt, though poison rack'd them through,
Remorse the deadlier torment of the two !
While some, the bravest, hardiest in the train
Of their false Chief, who on the battle-plain
Would have met death with transport by his side,
Here mute and helpless gasp'd ; but, as they died,
Look'd horrible vengeance with their eyes' last strain,
And clench'd the slackening hand at him in vain.

    Dreadful it was to see the ghastly stare,
The stony look of horror and despair,
Which some of these expiring victims cast
Upon their soul's tormentor to the last, —
Upon that mocking fiend, whose Veil, now raised,
Show'd them, as in death's agony they gazed,
Not the long-promised light, the brow, whose beaming
Was to come forth, all conquering, all redeeming,
But features horribler than hell e'er traced
On its own brood ; — no demon of the waste,
No churchyard ghole, caught lingering in the light
Of the bless'd sun, e'er blasted human sight
With lineaments so foul, so fierce, as those
Th' impostor now, in grinning mockery, shows :
"There, ye wise saints, behold your Light, your
        Star, —

Ye *would* be dupes and victims, and ye *are*.
Is it enough? or must I, while a thrill
Lives in your sapient bosoms, cheat you still?
Swear that the burning death ye feel within
Is but the trance with which heaven's joys begin;
That this foul visage, foul as e'er disgraced
Even monstrous man, is — after God's own taste;
And that — but see! — ere I have half-way said
My greetings through, th' uncourteous souls are fled.
Farewell, sweet spirits! not in vain ye die,
If Eblis loves you half so well as I. —
Ha, my young bride! — 'tis well, — take thou thy
      seat;
Nay, come — no shuddering — didst thou never meet
The dead before? — they graced our wedding, sweet;
And these, my guests to-night, have brimm'd so true
Their parting cups, that *thou* shalt pledge one too.
But — how is this? — all empty? all drunk up?
Hot lips have been before thee in the cup,
Young bride, — yet stay — one precious drop remains,
Enough to warm a gentle Priestess' veins;
Here, drink, — and should thy lover's conquering
      arms
Speed hither, ere thy lip lose all its charms,
Give him but half this venom in thy kiss,
And I'll forgive my haughty rival's bliss!

  " For *me* — I too must die; but not like these
Vile, rankling things, to fester in the breeze, —
To have this brow in ruffian triumph shown,
With all death's grimness added to its own,

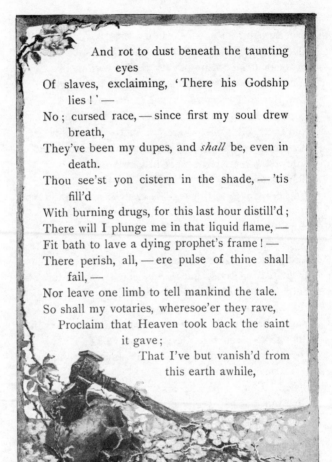

And rot to dust beneath the taunting
eyes
Of slaves, exclaiming, 'There his Godship
lies!'—
No; cursed race,—since first my soul drew
breath,
They've been my dupes, and *shall* be, even in
death.
Thou see'st yon cistern in the shade,—'tis
fill'd
With burning drugs, for this last hour distill'd;
There will I plunge me in that liquid flame,—
Fit bath to lave a dying prophet's frame!—
There perish, all,—ere pulse of thine shall
fail,—
Nor leave one limb to tell mankind the tale.
So shall my votaries, wheresoe'er they rave,
Proclaim that Heaven took back the saint
it gave;
That I've but vanish'd from
this earth awhile,

To come again with bright unshrouded smile!
So shall they build me altars in their zeal,
Where knaves shall minister and fools shall kneel;
Where Faith may mutter o'er her mystic spell,
Written in blood, and Bigotry may swell
The sail he spreads for heaven with blasts from hell!
So shall my banner through long ages be
The rallying sign of fraud and anarchy;
Kings yet unborn shall rue Mokanna's name,
And, though I die, my spirit, still the same,
Shall walk abroad in all the stormy strife,
And guilt, and blood, that were its bliss in life!
But, hark! their battering-engine shakes the wall —
Why, *let* it shake — thus I can brave them all.
No trace of me shall greet them, when they come,
And I can trust thy faith, for — thou'lt be dumb.
Now mark how readily a wretch like me,
In one bold plunge, commences Deity!" —

He sprung and sunk, as the last words were said:
Quick closed the burning waters o'er his head,
And Zelica was left — within the ring
Of those wide walls the only living thing;
The only wretched one, still cursed with breath,
In all that frightful wilderness of death!
More like some bloodless ghost, — such as, they tell,
In the lone Cities of the Silent dwell,
And there, unseen by all but Alla, sit
Each by its own pale carcass, watching it.

But morn is up, and a fresh warfare stirs
Throughout the camp of the beleaguerers.

Their globes of fire (the dread artillery, lent
By Greece to conquering Mahadi) are spent;
And now the scorpion's shaft, the quarry sent

From high ballistas,
and the shielded
throng
Of soldiers swinging
the huge ram
along, —
All speak th' impa-
tient Islamite's in-
tent
To try, at length, if
tower and battle-
ment
And bastion'd wall be
not less hard to
win,
Less tough to break
down, than the
hearts within.
First in impatience
and in toil is he,
The burning Azim —
oh! could he but
see
Th' impostor once
alive within his
grasp,
Not the gaunt lion's
hug, nor boa's clasp,

Could match that gripe of vengeance, or keep pace
With the fell heartiness of hate's embrace!

    Loud rings the ponderous ram against the walls;
Now shake the ramparts, now a buttress falls,
But still no breach — "Once more, one mighty swing
Of all your beams, together thundering!"
There — the wall shakes; the shouting troops exult —
"Quick, quick discharge your weightiest catapult
Right on that spot, and Neksheb is our own!"
'Tis done, — the battlements come crashing down :
And the huge wall, by that stroke riven in two,
Yawning like some old crater, rent anew,
Shows the dim, desolate city smoking through!
But strange! no signs of life, — nought living seen
Above, below, — what can this stillness mean?
A minute's pause suspends all hearts and eyes —
"In through the breach," impetuous Azim cries;
But the cool Caliph, fearful of some wile
In this blank stillness, checks the troops awhile.
Just then a figure, with slow step, advanced
Forth from the ruin'd walls, and, as there glanced
A sunbeam over it, all eyes could see
The well-known Silver Veil! — "'Tis he, 'tis he,
Mokanna, and alone!" they shout around;
Young Azim from his steed springs to the ground —
"Mine, holy Caliph! mine," he cries, "the task
To crush yon daring wretch, — 'tis all I ask."
Eager he darts to meet the demon foe,
Who, still across wide heaps of ruin, slow
And falteringly comes, till they are near;

Then, with a bound, rushes on Azim's spear,
And casting off the Veil in falling, shows —
Oh! — 'tis his Zelica's life-blood that flows!

    " I meant not, Azim," soothingly she said,
As on his trembling arm she lean'd her head,
And, looking in his face, saw anguish there
Beyond all wounds the quivering flesh can bear —
" I meant not *thou* shouldst have the pain of this ; —
Though death, with thee thus tasted, is a bliss
Thou wouldst not rob me of, didst thou but know
How oft I've pray'd to God I might die so!
But the fiend's venom was too scant and slow ; —
To linger on were maddening — and I thought
If once that Veil — nay, look not on it — caught
The eyes of your fierce soldiery, I should be
Struck by a thousand death-darts instantly.
But this is sweeter — oh, believe me, yes —
I would not change this sad, but dear caress,
This death within thy arms I would not give
For the most smiling life the happiest live!
All, that stood dark and drear before the eye
Of my stray'd soul, is passing swiftly by:
A light comes o'er me from those looks of love,
Like the first dawn of mercy from above ;
And if thy lips but tell me I'm forgiven,
Angels will echo the blest words in heaven!
But live, my Azim ; — oh! to call thee mine
Thus once again! *my* Azim — dream divine!
Live, if thou ever lovedst me, if to meet
Thy Zelica hereafter would be sweet, —

Oh, live to pray for her — to bend the knee
Morning and night before that Deity,
To whom pure lips and hearts without a stain,
As thine are, Azim, never breathed in vain, —
And pray that He may pardon her, — may take
Compassion on her soul for thy dear sake,
And nought remembering but her love to thee,
Make her all thine, all His, eternally!
Go to those happy fields where first we twined
Our youthful hearts together, — every wind
That meets thee there, fresh from the well-known
        flowers,
Will bring the sweetness of those innocent hours
Back to thy soul, and thou mayst feel again
For thy poor Zelica as thou didst then.
So shall thy orisons, like dew that flies
To heaven upon the morning's sunshine, rise
With all love's earliest ardour to the skies!
And should they — but alas! my senses fail —
Oh, for one minute! — should thy prayers prevail —
If pardon'd souls may from that World of Bliss
Reveal their joy to those they love in this, —
I'll come to thee — in some sweet dream — and tell —
O Heaven — I die — dear love! farewell, farewell."

Time fleeted, — years on years had pass'd away,
And few of those who on that mournful day
Had stood, with pity in their eyes, to see
The maiden's death and the youth's agony,
Were living still, — when, by a rustic grave
Beside the swift Amoo's transparent wave,

An aged man, who had grown aged there
By that lone grave, morning and night in prayer,
For the last time knelt down ; and, though the shade
Of death hung darkening over him, there play'd
A gleam of rapture on his eye and cheek,
That brighten'd even death, — like the last streak
Of intense glory on th' horizon's brim,
When night o'er all the rest hangs chill and dim,
His soul had seen a vision, while he slept;
She for whose spirit he had pray'd and wept
So many years, had come to him, all dress'd
In angel smiles, and told him she was blest !
For this the old man breathed his thanks, and died —
And there, upon the banks of that loved tide,
He and his Zelica sleep side by side.

THE story of the Veiled Prophet of Khorassan being ended, they were now doomed to hear Fadladeen's
criticisms upon it. A series of disappointments and
accidents had occurred to this learned Chamberlain
during the journey. In the first place, those couriers
stationed, as in the reign of Shah Jehan, between
Delhi and the western coast of India, to secure a constant supply of mangoes for the Royal Table, had,
by some cruel irregularity, failed in their duty ; and
to eat any mangoes but those of Mazagong was, of
course, impossible. In the next place, the elephant
laden with his fine antique porcelain had, in an unusual fit of liveliness, shattered the whole set to
pieces, — an irreparable loss, as many of the vessels
were so exquisitely old as to have been used under

the Emperors Yan and Chun, who reigned many
ages before the dynasty of Tang. His Koran too,
supposed to be the identical copy between the leaves
of which Mahomet's favourite pigeon used to nestle,
had been mislaid by his Koran-bearer three whole
days ; not without much spiritual alarm to Fadladeen, who, though professing to hold, with other loyal
and orthodox Mussulmans, that salvation could only
be found in the Koran, was strongly suspected of
believing in his heart that it could only be found in
his own particular copy of it. When to all these
grievances is added the obstinacy of the cooks, in
putting the pepper of Canara into his dishes instead
of the cinnamon of Serendib, we may easily suppose
that he came to the task of criticism with at least a
sufficient degree of irritability for the purpose.

"In order," said he, importantly swinging about
his chaplet of pearls, "to convey with clearness my
opinion of the story this young man has related, it is
necessary to take a review of all the stories that have
ever —" "My good Fadladeen !" exclaimed the
Princess, interrupting him, "we really do not deserve that you should give yourself so much trouble.
Your opinion of the poem we have just heard will,
I have no doubt, be abundantly edifying, without
any further waste of your valuable erudition." "If
that be all," replied the critic, evidently mortified at
not being allowed to show how much he knew about
everything but the subject immediately before him,
— "if that be all that is required, the matter is easily
despatched." He then proceeded to analyse the

poem, in that strain (so well known to the unfortunate bards of Delhi) whose censures were an infliction
from which few recovered, and whose very praises
were like the honey extracted from the bitter flowers
of the aloe. The chief personages of the story were,
if he rightly understood them, an ill-favoured gentleman, with a veil over his face; a young lady, whose
reason went and came according as it suited the
poet's convenience to be sensible or otherwise; and
a youth in one of those hideous Bucharian bonnets,
who took the aforesaid gentleman in a veil for a
Divinity. "From such materials," said he, "what
can be expected? After rivalling each other in long
speeches and absurdities, through some thousands of
lines as indigestible as the filberds of Berdaa, our
friend in the veil jumps into a tub of aqua-fortis; the
young lady dies in a set speech, whose only recom-
mendation is that it is her last; and the lover lives
on to a good old age, for the laudable purpose of
seeing her ghost, which he at last happily accom-
plishes and expires. This, you will allow, is a fair
summary of the story; and if Nasser, the Arabian
merchant, told no better, our Holy Prophet (to whom
be all honour and glory!) had no need to be jealous
of his abilities for story-telling."

With respect to the style, it was worthy of the
matter; it had not even those politic contrivances
of structure which make up for the commonness of
the thoughts by the peculiarity of the manner, nor
that stately poetical phraseology by which sentiments
mean in themselves, like the blacksmith's apron con-

verted into a banner, are so easily gilt and embroidered
into consequence. Then, as to the versification it was,
to say no worse of it, execrable : it had neither the copi-
ous flow of Ferdosi, the sweetness of Hafez, nor the
sententious march of Sadi ; but appeared to him, in the
uneasy heaviness of its movements, to have been
modelled upon the gait of a very tired dromedary.
The licenses, too, in which it indulged were unpardon-
able ; for instance, this line, — and the poem abounded
with such : —

"Like the faint exquisite music of a dream."

"What critic that can count," said Fadladeen, "and
has his full complement of fingers to count withal,
would tolerate for an instant such syllabic superflui-
ties ? " —   He here looked round and discovered
that most of his audience were asleep ; while the
glimmering lamps seemed inclined to follow their
example.   It became necessary, therefore, however
painful to himself, to put an end to his valuable
animadversions for the present, and he accordingly
concluded, with an air of dignified candour, thus :
"Notwithstanding the observations which I have
thought it my duty to make, it is by no means my
wish to discourage the young man ; — so far from
it, indeed, that if he will but totally alter his style
of writing and thinking, I have very little doubt that
I shall be vastly pleased with him."

Some days elapsed, after this harangue of the Great
Chamberlain, before Lalla Rookh could venture to ask

for another story. The youth was still a welcome
guest in the pavilion, — to *one* heart, perhaps, too
dangerously welcome, — but all mention of poetry was,
as if by common consent, avoided. Though none of
the party had much respect for Fadladeen, yet his
censures, thus magisterially delivered, evidently made
an impression on them all. The Poet himself, to
whom criticism was quite a new operation (being
wholly unknown in that Paradise of the Indies, Cashmere), felt the shock as it is generally felt at first, till
use has made it more 'tolerable to the patient; the
ladies began to suspect that they ought not to be
pleased, and seemed to conclude that there must have
been much good sense in what Fadladeen said, from
its having set them all so soundly to sleep; while the
self-complacent Chamberlain was left to triumph in
the idea of having, for the hundred and fiftieth time
in his life, extinguished a Poet. Lalla Rookh alone
— and Love knew why — persisted in being delighted
with all she had heard, and in resolving to hear more
as speedily as possible.   Her manner, however, of first
returning to the subject was unlucky.   It was while
they rested during the heat of noon near a fountain,
on which some hand had rudely traced those well-
known words from the Garden of Sadi, — " Many, like
me, have viewed this fountain ; but they are gone, and
their eyes are closed for ever ! " — that she took occasion, from the melancholy beauty of this passage, to
dwell upon the charms of poetry in general.   " It is
true," she said, " few poets can imitate that sublime
bird which flies always in the air, and never touches

the earth : it is only once in many ages a Genius
appears, whose words, like those on the Written Mountain, last for ever ; but still there are some, as delightful perhaps, though not so wonderful, who, if not stars
over our head, are at least flowers along our path, and
whose sweetness of the moment we ought gratefully to
inhale, without calling upon them for a brightness and
a durability beyond their nature. In short," continued
she, blushing, as if conscious of being caught in an
oration, " it is quite cruel that a poet cannot wander
through his regions of enchantment, without having a
critic for ever, like the Old Man of the Sea, upon his
back !" Fadladeen, it was plain, took this last luckless
allusion to himself, and would treasure it up in his
mind as a whetstone for his next criticism. A sudden
silence ensued ; and the Princess, glancing a look at
Feramorz, saw plainly she must wait for a more cour-
ageous moment.

But the glories of Nature, and her wild, fragrant
airs, playing freshly over the current of youthful
spirits, will soon heal even deeper wounds than the
dull Fadladeens of this world can inflict. In an evening or two after, they came to the small Valley of
Gardens, which had been planted by order of the
Emperor for his favourite sister Rochinara, during their
progress to Cashmere, some years before ; and never
was there a more sparkling assemblage of sweets,
since the Gulzar-e-Irem, or Rose-bower of Irem. Every
precious flower was there to be found, that poetry or
love or religion has ever consecrated ; from the dark
hyacinth, to which Hafez compares his mistress's hair,

to the *Cámalatá*, by whose rosy blossoms the heaven
of Indra is scented.   As they sat in the cool fragrance
of this delicious spot, and Lalla Rookh remarked that
she could fancy it the abode of that Flower-loving
Nymph whom they worship in the temples of Kathay,
or of one of those Peris, those beautiful creatures of
the air, who live upon perfumes, and to whom a place
like this might make some amends for the Paradise
they have lost, — the young Poet, in whose eyes she
appeared, while she spoke, to be one of the bright
spiritual creatures she was describing, said hesitatingly
that he remembered a Story of a Peri, which, if the
Princess had no objection, he would venture to relate.
" It is," said he, with an appealing look to Fadladeen,
" in a lighter and humbler strain than the other; "
then, striking a few careless but melancholy chords on
his kitar, he thus began :

ONE morn a Peri at the gate
Of Eden stood, disconsolate;
And as she listened to the
    Springs
    Of Life within, like music
    flowing,
And caught the light upon her
    wings
    Through the half-open portal
    glowing,
She wept to think her recreant
    race
Should e'er have lost that glori-
    ous place!

"How happy," exclaim'd this
    child of air,
"Are the holy spirits who
    wander there,
    'Mid flowers that never shall
    fade or fall!

Though mine are the gardens of earth and sea,
And the stars themselves have flowers for me,
   One blossom of heaven out-blooms them all!
Though sunny the Lake of cool Cashmere,
With its plane-tree isle reflected clear,
   And sweetly the founts of that valley fall ;
Though bright are the waters of Sing-su-hay,
And the golden floods, that thitherward stray, —
Yet — oh, 'tis only the blest can say
   How the waters of heaven outshine them all!
Go, wing thy flight from star to star,
From world to luminous world, as far
   As the universe spreads its flaming wall ;
Take all the pleasures of all the spheres,
And multiply each through endless years,
   One minute of heaven is worth them all ! "

The glorious Angel who was keeping
The gates of Light, beheld her weeping ;
And as he nearer drew and listen'd
To her sad song, a tear-drop glisten'd
Within his eyelids, like the spray
   From Eden's fountain, when it lies
On the blue flower which — Bramins say —
   Blooms nowhere but in Paradise !
"Nymph of a fair, but erring line ! "
Gently he said, " one hope is thine, —
'Tis written in the Book of Fate, —
   The Peri yet may be forgiven
Who brings to this Eternal Gate
   The Gift that is most dear to Heaven!

Go, seek it, and redeem thy sin ; —
'Tis sweet to let the Pardon'd in ! "

Rapidly as comets run
To th' embraces of the sun ;
Fleeter than the starry brands
Flung at night from angel hands
At those dark and daring sprites
Who would climb th' empyreal heights, —
Down the blue vault the Peri flies,

And, lighted earthward by a glance
That just then broke from morning's eyes,
  Hung hovering o'er our world's expanse.

But whither shall the Spirit go
To find this gift for heaven? — "I know
The wealth," she cries, "of every urn,
In which unnumber'd rubies burn,
Beneath the pillars of Chilminar;
I know where the Isles of Perfume are,
Many a fathom down in the sea,
To the south of sun-bright Araby;
I know too where the Genii hid
The jewell'd cup of their king Jamshid,
With life's elixir sparkling high; —
But gifts like these are not for the sky.
Where was there ever a gem that shone
Like the steps of Alla's wonderful Throne?
And the Drops of Life— oh! what would they be
In the boundless Deep of Eternity?"

While thus she mused, her pinions fann'd
The air of that sweet Indian land,
Whose air is balm; whose ocean spreads
O'er coral rocks and amber beds;
Whose mountains, pregnant by the beam
Of the warm sun, with diamonds teem;
Whose rivulets are like rich brides,
Lovely, with gold beneath their tides;
Whose sandal groves and bowers of spice
Might be a Peri's Paradise!

But crimson now her rivers ran
   With human blood, — the smell of death
Came reeking from their spicy bowers ;
And man, the sacrifice of man,
   Mingled his taint with every breath
Upwafted from the innocent flowers !
Land of the Sun ! what foot invades
Thy pagods and thy pillar'd shades, —
Thy cavern shrines, and idol stones,
Thy monarchs and their thousand thrones ?
'Tis he of Gazna ; — fierce in wrath
   He comes, and India's diadems
Lie scatter'd in his ruinous path, —
   His bloodhounds he adorns with gems,
Torn from the violated necks
   Of many a young and loved Sultana ;
   Maidens within their pure Zenana,
   Priests in the very fane he slaughters,
And chokes up with the glittering wrecks
   Of golden shrines the sacred waters !

Downward the Peri turns her gaze,
And through the war-field's bloody haze
Beholds a youthful warrior stand,
   Alone, beside his native river, —
The red blade broken in his hand
   And the last arrow in his quiver.
" Live," said the conqueror, — " live to share
The trophies and the crowns I bear ! "
Silent that youthful warrior stood ,
Silent he pointed to the flood

All crimson with his country's
    blood,
Then sent his last remaining
    dart,
For answer, to th' invader's
    heart.

False flew the shaft, though
    pointed well;
The tyrant lived, the hero
    fell! —
Yet mark'd the Peri where he
    lay;
  And when the rush of war
    was past,
Swiftly descending on a ray
  Of morning light, she caught
    the last —
Last glorious drop his heart had
    shed,
Before its free-born spirit fled!

"Be this," she cried, as she
    wing'd her flight,

" My welcome gift at the Gates of Light.
Though foul are the drops that oft distil
  On the field of warfare, blood like this,
  For liberty shed, so holy is,
It would not stain the purest rill
  That sparkles among the bowers of bliss!
Oh! if there be, on this earthly sphere,
A boon, an offering, Heaven holds dear,
'Tis the last libation Liberty draws
From the heart that bleeds and breaks in her
    cause!"

" Sweet," said the Angel, as she gave
  The gift into his radiant hand,
" Sweet is our welcome of the brave
  Who die thus for their native land;
But see, — alas! — the crystal bar
Of Eden moves not, — holier far
Than e'en this drop the boon must be,
That opes the Gates of Heaven for thee!"
Her first fond hope of Eden blighted,
  Now among Afric's Lunar Mountains,
Far to the south, the Peri lighted;
  And sleek'd her plumage at the fountains
Of that Egyptian tide whose birth
Is hidden from the sons of earth,
Deep in those solitary woods
Where oft the Genii of the Floods
Dance round the cradle of their Nile,
And hail the new-born Giant's smile!
Thence, over Egypt's palmy groves

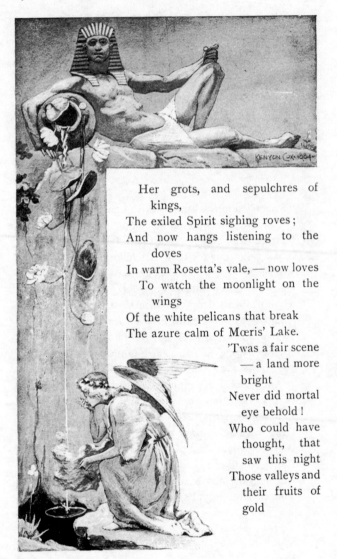

Her grots, and sepulchres of kings,
The exiled Spirit sighing roves;
And now hangs listening to the doves
In warm Rosetta's vale, — now loves
    To watch the moonlight on the wings
Of the white pelicans that break
The azure calm of Mœris' Lake.

'Twas a fair scene — a land more bright
Never did mortal eye behold!
Who could have thought, that saw this night
Those valleys and their fruits of gold

Basking in heaven's serenest light;
Those groups of lovely date-trees bending
   Languidly their leaf-crown'd heads,
Like youthful maids, when sleep descending
   Warns them to their silken beds;
Those virgin lilies, all the night
   Bathing their beauties in the lake,
That they may rise more fresh and bright,
   When their beloved sun's awake;
Those ruin'd shrines and towers that seem
The relics of a splendid dream,
   Amid whose fairy loneliness
Nought but the lapwing's cry is heard,
Nought seen but (when the shadows, flitting
Fast from the moon, unsheathe its gleam)
Some purple-wing'd sultana sitting
   Upon a column, motionless
And glittering, like an idol bird! —
Who could have thought that there, e'en there,
Amid those scenes so still and fair,
The Demon of the Plague hath cast
From his hot wing a deadlier blast,
More mortal far than ever came
From the red desert's sands of flame!
So quick, that every living thing
Of human shape, touch'd by his wing,
Like plants where the simoom hath past,
At once falls black and withering!
The sun went down on many a brow
   Which, full of bloom and freshness then,
Is rankling in the pest-house now,

And ne'er will feel that sun again
And oh! to see the unburied heaps
On which the lonely midnight sleeps —
The very vultures turn away,
And sicken at so foul a prey!
Only the fierce hyena stalks
Throughout the city's desolate walks
At midnight, and his carnage plies —
  Woe to the half-dead wretch, who meets
The glaring of those large blue eyes
  Amid the darkness of the streets!

" Poor race of Men!" said the pitying Spirit,
  " Dearly ye pay for your primal fall, —
Some flowerets of Eden ye still inherit,
  But the trail of the Serpent is over them all!"
She wept, — the air grew pure and clear
  Around her, as the bright drops ran;
For there's a magic in each tear,
  Such kindly spirits weep for man!

Just then, beneath some orange-trees,
Whose fruit and blossoms in the breeze
Were wantoning together, free,
Like age at play with infancy, —
Beneath that fresh and springing bower,
  Close by the lake, she heard the moan
Of one who, at this silent hour,
  Had thither stolen to die alone:
One who in life, where'er he moved,
  Drew after him the hearts of many;

Yet now, as though he
ne'er were loved,
Dies here unseen, un-
wept by any!
None to watch near
him, — none to
slake
The fire that in his
bosom lies,
With e'en a sprinkle
from that lake
Which shines so cool
before his eyes;

No voice, well known through many a day,
    To speak the last, the parting word,
Which, when all other sounds decay,
    Is still like distant music heard,
That tender farewell on the shore
Of this rude world, when all is o'er,
Which cheers the spirit, ere its bark
Puts off into the unknown dark.

Deserted youth ! one thought alone
    Shed joy around his soul in death, —
That she whom he for years had known
And loved, and might have call'd his own,
    Was safe from this foul midnight's breath ;
Safe in her father's princely halls,
Where the cool airs from fountain falls,
Freshly perfumed by many a brand
Of the sweet wood from India's land,
Were pure as she whose brow they fann'd.

But see, — who yonder comes by stealth,
    This melancholy bower to seek,
Like a young envoy, sent by Health,
    With rosy gifts upon her cheek ?
'Tis she, — far off, through moonlight dim,
    He knew his own betrothèd bride, —
She, who would rather die with him
    Than live to gain the world beside ! —
Her arms are round her lover now,
    His livid cheeks to hers she presses,

And dips, to bind his burning brow,
  In the cool lake her loosen'd tresses.
Ah! once how little did he think
An hour would come when he should shrink
With horror from that dear embrace,
  Those gentle arms, that were to him
Holy as is the cradling place
  Of Eden's infant cherubim!
And now he yields — now turns away,
Shuddering as if the venom lay
All in those proffer'd lips alone, —
Those lips that, then so fearless grown,
Never until that instant came
Near his unask'd or without shame.
"Oh! let me only breathe the air,
  The blessed air, that's breathed by thee
And, whether on its wings it bear
  Healing or death, 'tis sweet to me!
There, — drink my tears, while yet they fall, —
  Would that my bosom's blood were balm,

And, well thou know'st, I'd shed it all
    To give thy brow one minute's calm.
Nay, turn not from me that dear face —
    Am I not thine, — thy own loved bride, —
The one, the chosen one, whose place
    In life or death is by thy side !
Think'st thou that she, whose only light
    In this dim world from thee hath shone,
Could bear the long, the cheerless night
    That must be hers when thou art gone ?
That I can live, and let thee go,
Who art my life itself ?   No, no —
When the stem dies, the leaf that grew
Out of its heart must perish too !
Then turn to me, my own love, turn,
Before like thee I fade and burn ;
Cling to these yet cool lips, and share
The last pure life that lingers there ! "
She fails — she sinks — as dies the lamp
In charnel airs or cavern damp,
So quickly do his baleful sighs
Quench all the sweet light of her eyes !
One struggle — and his pain is past, —
    Her lover is no longer living !
One kiss the maiden gives, — one last,
    Long kiss, which she expires in giving !

" Sleep," said the Peri, as softly she stole
The farewell sigh of that vanishing soul,
As true as e'er warm'd a woman's breast, —
" Sleep on, in visions of odour rest,

In balmier airs than ever yet stirr'd
Th' enchanted pile of that holy bird
Who sings at the last his own death-lay,
And in music and perfume dies away !''

Thus saying, from her lips she spread
    Unearthly breathings through the place,
And shook her sparkling wreath, and shed
    Such lustre o'er each paly face,
That like two lovely saints they seem'd
    Upon the eve of doomsday taken
From their dim graves, in odour sleeping ;
While that benevolent Peri beam'd
Like their good angel, calmly keeping
    Watch o'er them, till their souls would waken !
But morn is blushing in the sky ;
    Again the Peri soars above,
Bearing to heaven that precious sigh
    Of pure self-sacrificing love.
High throbb'd her heart, with hope elate,
    The Elysian palm she soon shall win,
For the bright Spirit at the gate

Smiled as she gave that offering in;
And she already hears the trees
    Of Eden, with their crystal bells
Ringing in that ambrosial breeze
    That from the Throne of Alla swells;
And she can see the starry bowls
    That lie around that lucid lake
Upon whose banks admitted souls
    Their first sweet draught of glory take!
But ah! even Peris' hopes are vain.
Again the Fates forbade, again
The immortal barrier closed: " Not yet,"
The Angel said as, with regret,
He shut from her that glimpse of glory.
" True was the maiden, and her story,
Written in light o'er Alla's head,
By seraph eyes shall long be read;
But, Peri, see, — the crystal bar
Of Eden moves not, — holier far
Then even this sigh the boon must be
That opes the Gates of Heaven for thee."

Now, upon Syria's land of roses
Softly the light of eve reposes,
And, like a glory, the broad sun
Hangs over sainted Lebanon;
Whose head in wintry grandeur towers,
    And whitens with eternal sleet,
While summer, in a vale of flowers,
    Is sleeping rosy at his feet.
To one who look'd from upper air

O'er all th' enchanted regions there,
How beauteous must have been the glow,
The life, the sparkling from below!—
Fair gardens, shining streams, with ranks
Of golden melons on their banks,
More golden where the sunlight falls;
Gay lizards, glittering on the walls
Of ruin'd shrines, busy and bright,
As they were all alive with light;
And, yet more splendid, numerous flocks
Of pigeons, settling on the rocks,
With their rich restless wings, that gleam
Variously in the crimson beam
Of the warm west,—as if inlaid
With brilliants from the mine, or made
Of tearless rainbows, such as span
Th' unclouded skies of Peristan!
And then the mingling sounds that come,
Of shepherd's ancient reed, with hum
Of the wild bees of Palestine
   Banqueting through the flowery vales,—
And, Jordan, those sweet banks of thine,
   And woods, so full of nightingales!

But nought can charm the luckless Peri;
Her soul is sad,—her wings are weary:
Joyless she sees the sun look down
On that great Temple, once his own.
Whose lonely columns stand sublime,
   Flinging their shadows from on high,

Like dials, which the wizard, Time,
  Had raised to count his ages by!

Yet haply there may lie conceal'd
  Beneath those chambers of the sun,
Some amulet of gems, anneal'd
In upper fires, some tablet seal'd
  With the great name of Solomon,
Which, spell'd by her illumined eyes,
  May teach her where, beneath the moon,
  In earth or ocean, lies the boon,
  The charm that can restore so soon
  An erring Spirit to the skies!

Cheer'd by this hope, she bends her thither:
  Still laughs the radiant eye of heaven,
  Nor have the golden bowers of even
In the rich west begun to wither,
When, o'er the vale of Balbec winging
    Slowly, she sees a child at play,
Among the rosy wild-flowers singing,
  As rosy and as wild as they;
Chasing, with eager hands and eyes,
The beautiful blue damsel-flies,
That flutter'd round the jasmine stems,
Like wingèd flowers or flying gems; —
And near the boy, who, tired with play,
Now nestling 'mid the roses lay,
She saw a wearied man dismount
  From his hot steed, and on the brink
Of a small imaret's rustic fount

Impatient fling him down to drink.
Then swift his haggard brow he turn'd
    To the fair child, who fearless sat,
Though never yet hath daybeam burn'd
Upon a brow more fierce than that, —
Sullenly fierce, — a mixture dire,
Like thunder-clouds, of gloom and fire;
In which the Peri's eye could read
Dark tales of many a ruthless deed, —
The ruin'd maid, the shrine profaned,
Oaths broken, and the threshold stain'd
With blood of guests! — *there* written, all,
Black as the damning drops that fall
From the denouncing Angel's pen,
Ere Mercy weeps them out again!
Yet tranquil now that man of crime
(As if the balmy evening time
Soften'd his spirit) look'd and lay,
Watching the rosy infant's play;
Though still, whene'er his eye by chance
Fell on the boy's, its lurid glance
Met that unclouded, joyous gaze,
As torches that have burnt all night
Through some impure and godless rite,
    Encounter morning's glorious rays.

But hark! the vesper call to prayer,
As slow the orb of daylight sets,
Is rising sweetly on the air,
    From Syria's thousand minarets!
The boy has started from the bed

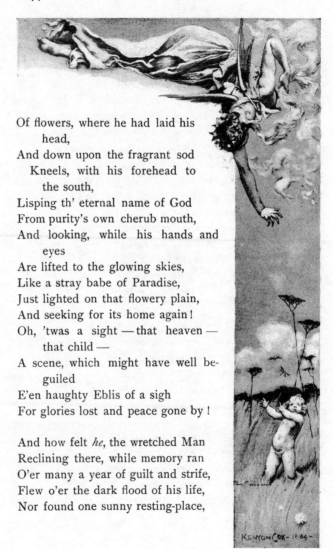

Of flowers, where he had laid his
     head,
And down upon the fragrant sod
   Kneels, with his forehead to
        the south,
Lisping th' eternal name of God
From purity's own cherub mouth,
And looking, while his hands and
     eyes
Are lifted to the glowing skies,
Like a stray babe of Paradise,
Just lighted on that flowery plain,
And seeking for its home again!
Oh, 'twas a sight — that heaven —
     that child —
A scene, which might have well be-
     guiled
E'en haughty Eblis of a sigh
For glories lost and peace gone by!

And how felt *he*, the wretched Man
Reclining there, while memory ran
O'er many a year of guilt and strife,
Flew o'er the dark flood of his life,
Nor found one sunny resting-place,

Nor brought him back one branch of grace?
"There *was* a time," he said, in mild,
Heart-humbled tones, "thou blessed child!
When, young and haply pure as thou,
I look'd and pray'd like thee; but now —"
He hung his head, — each nobler aim
   And hope and feeling, which had slept
From boyhood's hour, that instant came
   Fresh o'er him, and he wept — he wept!
Blest tears of soul-felt penitence!
   In whose benign, redeeming flow
Is felt the first, the only sense
   Of guiltless joy that guilt can know.

"There's a drop," said the Peri, "that down from
    the moon
Falls through the withering airs of June
Upon Egypt's land, of so healing a power,
So balmy a virtue, that e'en in the hour
That drop descends, contagion dies,
And health reanimates earth and skies! —
Oh! is it not thus, thou man of sin,
   The precious tears of repentance fall?
Though foul thy fiery plagues within,
   One heavenly drop hath dispell'd them all!"

And now — behold him kneeling there
By the child's side, in humble prayer,
While the same sunbeam shines upon
The guilty and the guiltless one,
And hymns of joy proclaim through heaven
The triumph of a soul forgiven!

'Twas when the golden orb had set,
While on their knees they linger'd yet,
There fell a light, more lovely far
Than ever came from sun or star,
Upon the tear that, warm and meek,
Dew'd that repentant sinner's cheek:
To mortal eye this light might seem
A northern flash or meteor beam;
But well th' enraptured Peri knew
'Twas a bright smile the Angel threw
From heaven's gate, to hail that tear
Her harbinger of glory near!

"Joy, joy for ever! my task is done, —
The Gates are pass'd, and heaven is won!
Oh! am I not happy?   I am, I am —
    To thee, sweet Eden! how dark and sad
Are the diamond turrets of Shadukiam,
    And the fragrant bowers of Amberabad!
Farewell, ye odours of earth, that die,
Passing away like a lover's sigh!
My feast is now of the tooba-tree,
Whose scent is the breath of eternity!

" Farewell, ye vanishing flowers, that shone
    In my fairy wreath, so bright and brief, —
Oh ! what are the brightest that e'er have blown,
To the lote-tree, springing by Alla's Throne,
    Whose flowers have a soul in every leaf !
Joy, joy for ever ! — my task is done, —
The Gates are pass'd, and heaven is won ! "

" AND this," said the Great Chamberlain, " is
poetry ! this flimsy manufacture of the brain, which,
in comparison with the lofty and durable monuments
of genius, is as the gold filigree-work of Zamara
beside the eternal architecture of Egypt." After this
gorgeous sentence, which, with a few more of the
same kind, Fadladeen kept by him for rare and important occasions, he proceeded to the anatomy of
the short poem just recited. The lax and easy kind
of metre in which it was written ought to be de-
nounced, he said, as one of the leading causes of the
alarming growth of poetry in our times. If some
check were not given to this lawless facility, we should
soon be overrun by a race of bards as numerous and
as shallow as the hundred and twenty thousand streams
of Basra. They who succeeded in this style deserved
chastisement for their very success ; — as warriors have
been punished, even after gaining a victory, because
they had taken the liberty of gaining it in an irregular
or unestablished manner. What, then, was to be said
to those who failed ? to those who presumed, as in the
present lamentable instance, to imitate the license and
ease of the bolder sons of song, without any of that

grace or vigour which gave a dignity even to negligence; who, like them, flung the jereed carelessly, but
not, like them, to the mark; "and who," said he, rais-
ing his voice to excite a proper degree of wakefulness
in his hearers, "contrive to appear heavy and con-
strained in the midst of all the latitude they have
allowed themselves, like one of those young pagans
that dance before the Princess, who has the ingenuity
to move as if her limbs were fettered in a pair of the
lightest and loosest drawers of Masulipatam !"

It was but little suitable, he continued, to the grave
march of criticism to follow this fantastical Peri, of
whom they had just heard, through all her flights and
adventures between earth and heaven, but he could
not help adverting to the puerile conceitedness of the
Three Gifts which she is supposed to carry to the
skies, — a drop of blood, forsooth, a sigh, and a tear !
How the first of these articles was delivered into the
Angel's "radiant hand" he professed himself at a loss
to discover; and as to the safe carriage of the sigh
and the tear, such Peris and such poets were beings
by far too incomprehensible for him even to guess
how they managed such matters. "But, in short,"
said he, "it is a waste of time and patience to dwell
longer upon a thing so incurably frivolous, — puny
even among its own puny race, and such as only the
Banyan Hospital for Sick Insects should undertake."

In vain did Lalla Rookh try to soften this inexora-
ble critic; in vain did she resort to her most eloquent
commonplaces, — reminding him that poets were a
timid and sensitive race, whose sweetness was not to

be drawn forth, like that of the fragrant grass near the Ganges, by crushing and trampling upon them ; that severity often destroyed every chance of the perfection which it demanded ; and that, after all, perfection was like the Mountain of the Talisman, — no one had ever yet reached its summit. Neither these gentle axioms, nor the still gentler looks with which they were inculcated, could lower for one instant the elevation of Fadladeen's eyebrows, or charm him into anything like encouragement, or even toleration, of her Poet. Toleration, indeed, was not among the weaknesses of Fadladeen : he carried the same spirit into matters of poetry and of religion, and, though little versed in the beauties or sublimities of either, was a perfect master of the art of persecution in both. His zeal, too, was the same in either pursuit, whether the game before him was pagans or poetasters, — worshippers of cows, or writers of epics.

They had now arrived at the splendid city of Lahore, whose mausoleums and shrines, magnificent and numberless, where Death seemed to share equal honours with Heaven, would have powerfully affected the heart and imagination of Lalla Rookh, if feelings more of this earth had not taken entire possession of her already. She was here met by messengers, despatched from Cashmere, who informed her that the King had arrived in the valley, and was himself superintending the sumptuous preparations that were making in the saloons of the Shalimar for her reception. The chill she felt on receiving this intelligence — which to a bride whose heart was free and light

would have brought only images of affection and
pleasure — convinced her that her peace was gone
for ever, and that she was in love, irretrievably in
love, with young Feramorz. The veil which this
passion wears at first had fallen off, and to know
that she loved was now as painful as to love *without*
knowing it had been delicious. Feramorz, too, —
what misery would be his, if the sweet hours of inter-
course so imprudently allowed them should have
stolen into his heart the same fatal fascination as into
hers; if, notwithstanding her rank and the modest
homage he always paid to it, even *he* should have
yielded to the influence of those long and happy inter-
views, where music, poetry, the delightful scenes of
nature, all tended to bring their hearts close together,
and to waken by every means that too ready passion,
which often, like the young of the desert-bird, is warmed
into life by the eyes alone! She saw but one way to
preserve herself from being culpable as well as unhappy; and this, however painful, she was resolved to
adopt. Feramorz must no more be admitted to her
presence. To have strayed so far into the dangerous
labyrinth was wrong; but to linger in it while the clew
was yet in her hand would be criminal. Though the
heart she had to offer to the King of Bucharia might
be cold and broken, it should at least be pure; and
she must only try to forget the short vision of happiness she had enjoyed, — like that Arabian shepherd
who, in wandering into the wilderness, caught a glimpse
of the Gardens of Irim, and then lost them again for
ever!

The arrival of the young Bride at Lahore was celebrated in the most enthusiastic manner. The rajas
and omras in her train, who had kept at a certain
distance during the journey, and never encamped
nearer to the Princess than was strictly necessary for
her safeguard, here rode in splendid cavalcade through
the city, and distributed the most costly presents to
the crowd. Engines were erected in all .the squares,
which cast forth showers of confectionery among the
people; while the artisans, in chariots adorned with
tinsel and flying streamers, exhibited the badges of
their respective trades through the streets. Such brilliant displays of life and pageantry among the palaces
and domes and gilded minarets of Lahore made the
city altogether like a place of enchantment; particularly on the day when Lalla Rookh set out again upon
her journey, when she was accompanied to the gate by
all the fairest and richest of the nobility, and rode
along between ranks of beautiful boys and girls, who
waved plates of gold and silver flowers over their heads
as they went, and then threw them to be gathered by
the populace.

For many days after their departure from Lahore,
a considerable degree of gloom hung over the whole
party. Lalla Rookh, who had intended to make ill-
ness her excuse for not admitting the young minstrel
as usual to the pavilion, soon found that to feign indis-
position was unnecessary; Fadladeen felt the loss of
the good road they had hitherto travelled, and was
very near cursing Jehan-Guire (of blessed memory!)
for not having continued his delectable alley of trees,

at least as far as the mountains of Cashmere; while the ladies, who had nothing now to do all day but to be fanned by peacocks' feathers and listen to Fadladeen, seemed heartily weary of the life they led, and, in spite of all the Great Chamberlain's criticisms, were tasteless enough to wish for the Poet again. One evening, as they were proceeding to their place of rest for the night, the Princess, who, for the freer enjoyment of the air, had mounted her favourite Arabian palfrey, in passing by a small grove heard the notes of a lute from within its leaves, and a voice, which she but too well knew, singing the following words:

> Tell me not of joys above,
>   If that world can give no bliss,
> Truer, happier than the love
>   Which enslaves our souls in this!
>
> Tell me not of Houris' eyes; —
>   Far from me their dangerous glow,
> If those looks that light the skies
>   Wound like some that burn below!
>
> Who that feels what love is here —
>   All its falsehood, all its pain —
> Would, for even elysium's sphere,
>   Risk the fatal dream again?
>
> Who, that midst a desert's heat
>   Sees the waters fade away,
> Would not rather die than meet
>   Streams again as false as they?

The tone of melancholy defiance in which these words were uttered went to Lalla Rookh's heart; and as she reluctantly rode on, she could not help feeling it as a sad but sweet certainty that Feramorz was to the full as enamoured and miserable as herself.

The place where they encamped that evening was the first delightful spot they had come to since they left Lahore. On one side of them was a grove full of small Hindoo temples, and planted with the most graceful trees of the East; where the tamarind, the cassia, and the silken plantains of Ceylon were mingled in rich contrast with the high fan-like foliage of the Palmyra, — that favourite tree of the luxurious bird that lights up the chambers of its nest with fireflies. In the middle of the lawn where the pavilion stood there was a tank surrounded by small mango-trees, on the clear cold waters of which floated multitudes of the beautiful red lotus, while at a distance stood the ruins of a strange and awful-looking tower, which seemed old enough to have been the temple of some religion no longer known, and which spoke the voice of desolation in the midst of all that bloom and loveliness. This singular ruin excited the wonder and conjectures of all. Lalla Rookh guessed in vain; and the all-pretending Fadladeen, who had never till this journey been beyond the precincts of Delhi, was proceeding most learnedly to show that he knew nothing whatever about the matter, when one of the ladies suggested that perhaps Feramorz could satisfy their curiosity. They were now approaching his native mountains, and this tower might be a relic of some of those dark superstitions, which had prevailed in that country before the light of Islam dawned upon it. The Chamberlain, who usually preferred his own ignorance to the best knowledge that any one else could give him, was by no means pleased with this officious reference; and the Princess, too, was about to interpose a faint word of objection : but, before either of them could speak, a slave was despatched for Feramorz, who in a very few minutes appeared before them, looking so pale and unhappy in Lalla Rookh's eyes, that she already repented of her cruelty in having so long excluded him.

That venerable tower, he told them, was the remains of an ancient Fire-Temple, built by those Ghebers or Persians of the old religion, who, many hundred years since, had fled hither from their Arab conquerors, preferring liberty and their altars in a foreign land to the alternative of apostasy or persecution in their own. It was impossible, he added, not to feel interested in the many glorious but unsuccessful struggles which had been made by these original natives of Persia to cast off the yoke of their bigoted conquerors. Like their own fire in the Burning Field at Bakou, when suppressed in one place, they had but broken out with fresh flame in another; and, as a native of Cashmere, of that fair and Holy Valley, which had in the same manner become the prey of strangers, and seen her ancient shrines and native princes swept away before the march of her intolerant invaders, he felt a sympathy, he owned, with the sufferings of the persecuted Ghebers, which every monument like this before them but tended more powerfully to awaken.

It was the first time that Feramorz had ever ventured upon so much *prose* before Fadladeen, and it may easily be conceived what effect such prose as this must have produced upon that most orthodox and most pagan-hating personage. He sat for some minutes aghast, ejaculating only at intervals, "Bigoted conquerors! — sympathy with Fire-worshippers!" — while Feramorz, happy to take advantage of this almost speechless horror of the Chamberlain, proceeded to say that he knew a melancholy story, connected with the events of one of those brave struggles of the Fire-worshippers of Persia against their Arab masters, which, if the evening was not too far advanced, he should have much pleasure in being allowed to relate to the Princess. It was impossible for Lalla Rookh to refuse; he had never before looked half so animated, and when he spoke of the Holy Valley his eyes had sparkled, she thought, like the talismanic characters on the cimeter of Solomon. Her consent was therefore most readily granted; and while Fadladeen sat in unspeakable dismay, expecting treason and abomination in every line, the poet thus began his story of the Fire-worshippers:

THE FIRE-WORSHIPPERS.

'Tis moonlight over Oman's Sea;
　　Her banks of pearl and palmy isles
Bask in the night-beam beauteously,
　　And her blue waters sleep in smiles.
'Tis moonlight in Harmozia's walls,
And through her Emir's porphyry halls,
Where, some hours since, was heard the swell
Of trumpet and the clash of zel,
Bidding the bright-eyed sun farewell, —

The peaceful sun, whom better suits
  The music of the bulbul's nest,
Or the light touch of lovers' lutes,
  To sing him to his golden rest !
All hush'd — there's not a breeze in motion ;
The shore is silent as the ocean.
If zephyrs come, so light they come,
  Nor leaf is stirr'd nor wave is driven ; —
The wind-tower on the Emir's dome.
  Can hardly win a breath from heaven.

Even he, that tyrant Arab, sleeps
Calm, while a nation round him weeps ;
While curses load the air he breathes,
And falchions from unnumber'd sheaths
Are starting to avenge the shame
His race hath brought on Iran's name.
Hard, heartless Chief, unmoved alike
'Mid eyes that weep, and swords that strike ; —
One of that saintly, murderous brood,
  To carnage and the Koran given,
Who think through unbelievers' blood
  Lies their directest path to heaven, —
One who will pause and kneel unshod
  In the warm blood his hand hath pour'd,
To mutter o'er some text of God
  Engraven on his reeking sword ;
Nay, who can coolly note the line,
The letter of those words divine,
To which his blade, with searching art,
Had sunk into its victim's heart !

Just Alla ! what must be thy look,
    When such a wretch before Thee stands
Unblushing, with thy Sacred Book, —
    Turning the leaves with blood-stain'd hands,
And wresting from its page sublime
His creed of lust and hate and crime ?
Even as those bees of Trebizond,
    Which from the sunniest flowers that glad
With their pure smile the gardens round,
    Draw venom forth that drives men mad !

Never did fierce Arabia send
    A satrap forth more direly great ;
Never was Iran doom'd to bend
    Beneath a yoke of deadlier weight.

Her throne had fallen ; her pride was crush'd ;
Her sons were willing slaves, nor blush'd,
In their own land, — no more their own, —
To crouch beneath a stranger's throne.
Her towers, where Mithra once had burn'd,
To Moslem shrines — oh, shame ! — were turn'd ;
Where slaves, converted by the sword,
Their mean, apostate worship pour'd,
And cursed the faith their sires adored.
Yet has she hearts, 'mid all this ill,
O'er all this wreck, high buoyant still
With hope and vengeance ; hearts that yet —
　　Like gems, in darkness issuing rays
They've treasured from the sun that's set —
　　Beam all the light of long-lost days !
And swords she hath, nor weak nor slow
　　To second all such hearts can dare ;
As he shall know, well, dearly know,
　　Who sleeps in moonlight luxury there,
Tranquil as if his spirit lay
Becalm'd in Heaven's approving ray !
Sleep on, — for purer eyes than thine
Those waves are hush'd, those planets shine.
Sleep on, — and be thy rest unmoved
　　By the white moonbeam's dazzling power ;
None but the loving and the loved
　　Should be awake at this sweet hour.

And see — where, high above those rocks
　　That o'er the deep their shadows fling,
Yon turret stands, — where ebon locks,

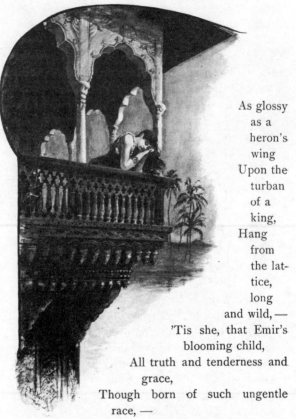

As glossy
as a
heron's
wing
Upon the
turban
of a
king,
Hang
from
the lat-
tice,
long
and wild, —
'Tis she, that Emir's
blooming child,
All truth and tenderness and
grace,
Though born of such ungentle
race, —
An image of Youth's fairy Fountain
Springing in a desolate mountain !

Oh, what a pure and sacred thing
Is beauty, curtain'd from the sight

Of the gross world, illumining
  One only mansion with her
    light!
    Unseen by man's disturbing eye, —
      The flower that blooms beneath the sea,
Too deep for sunbeams, doth not lie
    Hid in more chaste obscurity!
So, Hinda, have thy face and mind,
Like holy mysteries, lain enshrined.
And oh, what transport for a lover
    To lift the veil that shades them o'er!
Like those who all at once discover
    In the lone deep some fairy shore,
    Where mortal never trod before,
And sleep and wake in scented airs
No lip had ever breathed but theirs!
Beautiful are the maids that glide,
    On summer eves, through Yemen's dales,
And bright the glancing looks they hide

Behind their litters' roseate veils;
And brides, as delicate and fair
As the white jasmine flowers they wear,
Hath Yemen in her blissful clime,
   Who lull'd in cool kiosk or bower
Before their mirrors count the time,
   And grow still lovelier every hour.
But never yet hath bride or maid
   In Araby's gay harams smiled,
Whose boasted brightness would not fade
   Before Al Hassan's blooming child.

Light as the angel shapes that bless
An infant's dream, yet not the less
Rich in all woman's loveliness;
With eyes so pure, that from their ray
Dark vice would turn abash'd away,
Blinded like serpents, when they gaze
Upon the emerald's virgin blaze!
Yet, fill'd with all youth's sweet desires,
Mingling the meek and vestal fires
Of other worlds with all the bliss,
The fond, weak tenderness of this!
A soul, too, more than half divine,
   Where, through some shades of earthly feeling,
Religion's soften'd glories shine,
   Like light through summer foliage stealing,
Shedding a glow of such mild hue,
So warm, and yet so shadowy too,
As makes the very darkness there
More beautiful than light elsewhere!

Such is the maid who at this hour
    Hath risen from her restless sleep,
And sits alone in that high bower,
    Watching the still and shining deep.
Ah ! 'twas not thus — with tearful eyes
    And beating heart — she used to gaze
On the magnificent earth and skies,
    In her own land, in happier days.
Why looks she now so anxious down
Among those rocks, whose rugged frown
    Blackens the mirror of the deep?
Whom waits she all this lonely night?
    Too rough the rocks, too bold the steep,
For man to scale that turret's height !

So deem'd at least her thoughtful sire,
    When high, to catch the cool night air,
After the daybeam's withering fire,
    He built her bower of freshness there,
And had it deck'd with costliest skill,
    And fondly thought it safe as fair ; —
Think, reverend dreamer ! think so still,
    Nor wake to learn what love can dare, —
Love, all-defying Love, who sees
No charm in trophies won with ease ;
Whose rarest, dearest fruits of bliss
Are pluck'd on danger's precipice !
Bolder than they who dare not dive
    For pearls but when the sea's at rest,
Love, in the tempest most alive,
    Hath ever held that pearl the best

He finds beneath the stormiest water!
Yes, — Araby's unrivall'd daughter,
Though high that tower, that rock-way rude,
    There's one who, but to kiss thy cheek,
Would climb th' untrodden solitude
    Of Ararat's tremendous peak,
And think its steeps, though dark and
        dread,
Heaven's pathways, if to thee they led!
E'en now thou seest the flashing spray,
That lights his oar's impatient way;
E'en now thou hear'st the sudden shock
Of his swift bark against the rock,
And stretchest down thy arms of snow,
As if to lift him from below!
Like her to whom, at dead of night,
The bridegroom, with his locks of light,
Came, in the flush of love and pride,
And scaled the terrace of his bride;
When, as she saw him rashly spring,
And midway up in danger cling,
She flung him down her long black hair,
Exclaiming, breathless, " There, love, there!"
And scarce did manlier nerve uphold
    The hero Zal in that fond hour,
Than wings the youth who, fleet and bold,
    Now climbs the rocks to Hinda's bower.
See — light as up their granite steeps
    The rock-goats of Arabia clamber,
Fearless from crag to crag he leaps,
    And now is in the maiden's chamber.

She loves, — but knows not whom she loves,
  Nor what his race, nor whence he came ; —
Like one who meets, in Indian groves,
  Some beauteous bird, without a name,
Brought by the last ambrosial breeze,
From isles in th' undiscover'd seas,
To show his plumage for a day
To wondering eyes, and wing away !
Will *he* thus fly, — her nameless lover ?
  Alla forbid ! 'twas by a moon
As fair as this, while singing over
  Some ditty to her soft Kanoon,
Alone at this same witching hour,
  She first beheld his radiant eyes
Gleam through the lattice of the bower,
  Where nightly now they mix their sighs ;
And thought some spirit of the air
(For what could waft a mortal there ?)
Was pausing on his moonlight way
To listen to her lonely lay !

This fancy ne'er hath left her mind ;
  And though, when terror's swoon had past,
She saw a youth, of mortal kind,
  Before her in obeisance cast,
Yet often since, when he hath spoken
Strange, awful words, and gleams have broken
From his dark eyes, too bright to bear,
  Oh ! she hath fear'd her soul was given
To some unhallow'd child of air,
  Some erring spirit cast from heaven,

Like those angelic youths of old,
Who burn'd for maids of mortal mould,
Bewilder'd left the glorious skies,
And lost their heaven for woman's eyes!
Fond girl, nor fiend nor angel he,
Who woos thy young simplicity;
But one of earth's impassion'd sons,
   As warm in love, as fierce in ire,
As the best heart whose current runs
   Full of the Day-god's living fire!

But quench'd to-night that ardour seems,
   And pale his cheek, and sunk his brow; —
Never before, but in her dreams,
   Had she beheld him pale as now;
And those were dreams of troubled sleep,
From which 'twas joy to wake and weep, —
Visions, that will not be forgot,
   But sadden every waking scene,
Like warning ghosts, that leave the spot
   All wither'd where they once have been!

" How sweetly," said the trembling maid,
Of her own gentle voice afraid,
So long had they in silence stood,
Looking upon that tranquil flood, —
" How sweetly does the moonbeam smile
To-night upon yon leafy isle!
Oft, in my fancy's wanderings,
I've wish'd that little isle had wings,
And we, within its fairy bowers,

Were wafted off to seas unknown,
Where not a pulse should beat but ours,
    And we might live, love, die alone !
Far from the cruel and the cold, —
    Where the bright eyes of angels only
Should come around us to behold
    A paradise so pure and lonely !
Would this be world enough for thee ? "
Playful she turn'd, that he might see
    The passing smile her cheek put on !
But when she mark'd how mournfully
    His eyes met hers, that smile was gone ;
And, bursting into heartfelt tears,
" Yes, yes," she cried, " my hourly fears,
My dreams, have boded all too right —
We part — for ever part — to-night ! —
I knew, I knew it *could* not last —
'Twas bright, 'twas heavenly, but 'tis past !
Oh ! ever thus, from childhood's hour,
    I've seen my fondest hopes decay ;
I never loved a tree or flower,
    But 'twas the first to fade away.
I never nursed a dear gazelle,
    To glad me with its soft black eye,
But when it came to know me well,
    And love me, it was sure to die !
Now too — the joy most like divine
    Of all I ever dreamt or knew,
To see thee, hear thee, call thee mine, —
    Oh, misery ! must I lose *that* too ?
Yet go — on peril's brink we meet ; —

Those frightful rocks —
　　that treacherous sea —
No, never come again — though
　　sweet,
　　Though heaven, it may be death to thee.
Farewell — and blessings on thy way,
　　Where'er thou go'st, beloved stranger!
Better to sit and watch that ray,
And think thee safe, though far away,
　　Than have thee near me, and in danger!"

" Danger ! oh, tempt me not to boast,"
The youth exclaim'd, — " thou little know'st
What he can brave who, born and nurst
In Danger's paths, has dared her worst !
Upon whose ear the signal-word
    Of strife and death is hourly breaking ;
Who sleeps with head upon the sword
    His fever'd hand must grasp in waking !
Danger ! — "

                " Say on — thou fear'st not then,
And we may meet — oft meet again ? "

" Oh, look not so, — beneath the skies
I now fear nothing but those eyes.
If aught on earth could charm or force
My spirit from its destined course,
If aught could make this soul forget
The bond to which its seal is set,
'Twould be those eyes ; — they, only they,
Could melt that sacred seal away !
But no — 'tis fix'd — *my* awful doom
Is fix'd — on this side of the tomb
We meet no more — why, why did Heaven
Mingle two souls that earth has riven,
Has rent asunder, wide as ours ?
O Arab maid ! as soon the powers
Of light and darkness may combine,
As I be link'd with thee or thine !
Thy Father — "

" Holy Alla, save
    His gray head from that lightning glance !
Thou know'st him not, — he loves the brave ;
    Nor lives there under heaven's expanse
One who would prize, would worship thee,
And thy bold spirit, more than he.
Oft, when in childhood, I have play'd
    With the bright falchion by his side,
I've heard him swear his lisping maid
    In time should be a warrior's bride ;
And still, whene'er, at haram hours,
I take him cool sherbets and flowers,
He tells me, when in playful mood,
    A hero shall my bridegroom be,
Since maids are best in battle woo'd,

And won with shouts
   of victory !
Nay, turn not from me, — thou alone
Art form'd to make both hearts thy own.
Go — join his sacred ranks — thou know'st
   Th' unholy strife these Persians wage : —
Good Heaven, that frown ! — even now thou glow'st
   With more than mortal warrior's rage.
Haste to the camp by morning's light,
And, when that sword is raised in fight,
Oh, still remember, Love and I
Beneath its shadow trembling lie !
One victory o'er those Slaves of Fire,
Those impious Ghebers, whom my sire
Abhors — "

" Hold, hold — thy words are death,
    The stranger cried, as wild he flung
His mantle back, and show'd beneath
    The Gheber belt that round him clung —
" Here, maiden, look — weep — blush to see
All that thy sire abhors in me!
Yes — *I* am of that impious race,
    Those Slaves of Fire, who, morn and even,
Hail their Creator's dwelling-place
    Among the living lights of heaven!
Yes — *I* am of that outcast few,
To Iran and to vengeance true,
Who curse the hour your Arabs came
To desolate our shrines of flame,
And swear, before God's burning eye,
To break our country's chains, or die!
Thy bigot sire — nay, tremble not —
    He who gave birth to those dear eyes
With me is sacred as the spot
    From which our fires of worship rise!
But know — 'twas he I sought that night,
    When, from my watch-boat on the sea,
I caught this turret's glimmering light,
    And up the rude rocks desperately
Rush'd to my prey — thou know'st the rest —
I climb'd the gory vulture's nest,
And found a trembling dove within —
Thine, thine the victory — thine the sin —
If Love hath made one thought his own,
That vengeance claims first — last — alone!
Oh! had we never, never met,

Or could this heart e'en now forget
How link'd, how bless'd, we might have been,
Had fate not frown'd so dark between !
Hadst thou been born a Persian maid,
 In neighbouring valleys had we dwelt,
Through the same fields in childhood play'd,
 At the same kindling altar knelt, —
Then, then, while all those nameless ties,
In which the charm of country lies,
Had round our hearts been hourly spun,
Till Iran's cause and thine were one ; —
While in thy lute's awakening sigh
I heard the voice of days gone by,
And saw in every smile of thine
Returning hours of glory shine ! —
While the wrong'd Spirit of our Land
 Lived, look'd, and spoke her wrongs through
  thee, —
God ! who could then this sword withstand ?
 Its every flash were victory !
But now — estranged, divorced for ever,
Far as the grasp of Fate can sever,
Our only ties what love has wove, —
 Faith, friends, and country, sunder'd wide ;
And then, then only, true to love,
 When false to all that's dear beside !
Thy father, Iran's deadliest foe —
Thyself, perhaps, e'en now — but no —
Hate never look'd so lovely yet !
 No — sacred to thy soul will be
The land of him who could forget

All but that bleeding
land for thee !

When other eyes shall see, unmoved,
   Her widows mourn, her warriors fall,
Thou'lt think how well one Gheber loved,
   And for *his* sake thou'lt weep for all !
But look — "

       With sudden start he turn'd
   And pointed to the distant wave,
Where lights, like charnel meteors, burn'd
   Bluely, as o'er some seaman's grave ;
And fiery darts, at intervals,
   Flew up all sparkling from the main,
As if each star that nightly falls,
   Were shooting back to heaven again.
" My signal lights ! — I must away —
Both, both are ruin'd, if I stay.
Farewell — sweet life ! thou cling'st in vain —
Now — Vengeance ! I am thine again."
Fiercely he broke away, nor stopp'd
Nor look'd — but from the lattice dropp'd
Down 'mid the pointed crags beneath,
As if he fled from love to death.
While pale and mute young Hinda stood,
Nor moved, till in the silent flood
A momentary plunge below
Startled her from her trance of woe ;
Shrieking she to the lattice flew,
" I come — I come — if in that tide
Thou sleep'st to-night — I'll sleep there too,
   In death's cold wedlock by thy side.
Oh ! I would ask no happier bed

Than the chill wave my love lies under;
Sweeter to rest together dead,
    Far sweeter than to live asunder!"
But no, — their hour is not yet come, —
    Again she sees his pinnace fly,
Wafting him fleetly to his home,
    Where'er that ill-starr'd home may lie;

And calm and smooth it seem'd to win
   Its moonlight way before the wind,
As it bore all peace within,
   Nor left one breaking heart behind !

THE Princess, whose heart was sad enough already,
could have wished that Feramorz had chosen a less
melancholy story ; as it is only to the happy that tears
are a luxury. Her ladies, however, were by no means
sorry that love was once more the poet's theme ; for
when he spoke of love, they said, his voice was as
sweet as if he had chewed the leaves of that enchanted
tree which grows over the tomb of the musician Tan-
Sein.

Their road all the morning had lain through a very
dreary country, — through valleys, covered with a low
bushy jungle, where, in more than one place, the awful
signal of the bamboo staff, with the white flag at its
top, reminded the traveller that in that very spot the
tiger had made some human creature his victim. It
was therefore with much pleasure that they arrived at
sunset in a safe and lovely glen, and encamped under
one of those holy trees whose smooth columns and
spreading roofs seem to destine them for natural
temples of Religion. Beneath the shade, some pious
hands had erected pillars ornamented with the most
beautiful porcelain, which now supplied the use of
mirrors to the young ladies, as they adjusted their hair
in descending from the palankeens. Here, while, as
usual, the Princess sat listening anxiously, with Fadladeen in one of his loftiest moods of criticism by her

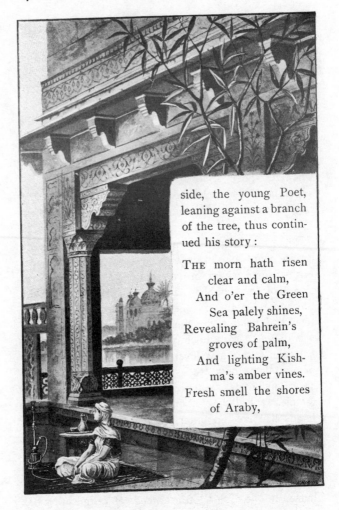

side, the young Poet,
leaning against a branch
of the tree, thus contin-
ued his story :

THE morn hath risen
    clear and calm,
    And o'er the Green
    Sea palely shines,
Revealing Bahrein's
    groves of palm,
    And lighting Kish-
    ma's amber vines.
Fresh smell the shores
    of Araby,

While breezes from the Indian sea
Blow round Selama's sainted
cape,
And curl the shining flood
beneath,
Whose waves are rich with
many a grape,
A cocoa-nut, and flowery
wreath,
Which pious seamen, as they
pass'd,
Had toward that holy head-
land cast, —
Oblations to the Genii
there

For gentle skies and breezes fair !
The nightingale now bends her flight
From the high trees, where all the night
   She sung so sweet, with none to listen ;
And hides her from the morning star
   Where thickets of pomegranate glisten
In the clear dawn, — bespangled o'er
   With dew, whose night-drops would not stain
The best and brightest cimeter
That ever youthful Sultan wore
   On the first morning of his reign !

And see — the Sun himself ! — on wings
Of glory up the east he springs.
Angel of light ! who from the time
Those heavens began their march sublime,
Hath first of all the starry choir
Trod in his Maker's steps of fire !
   Where are the days, thou wondrous sphere,
When Iran, like a sunflower turn'd
To meet that eye, where'er it burn'd ? —
   When, from the banks of Bendemeer
To the nut-groves of Samarcand,
Thy temples flamed o'er all the land ?
Where are they ? ask the shades of them
   Who on Cadessia's bloody plains
Saw fierce invaders pluck the gem
From Iran's broken diadem,
   And bind her ancient faith in chains ; —
Ask the poor exile, cast alone
On foreign shores, unloved, unknown,

Beyond the Caspian's Iron Gates,
  Or on the snowy Mossian mountains,
Far from his beauteous land of dates,
  Her jasmine bowers and sunny fountains !
Yet happier so than if he trod
His own beloved but blighted sod,
Beneath a despot stranger's nod ! —
Oh ! he would rather houseless roam
  Where freedom and his God may lead,
Than be the sleekest slave at home
  That crouches to the conqueror's creed !
Is Iran's pride then gone for ever,
  Quench'd with the flame in Mithra's caves ? —
No : she has sons that never — never —
  Will stoop to be the Moslem's slaves,
  While heaven has light or earth has graves.
Spirits of fire, that brood not long,
But flash resentment back for wrong ;
And hearts where, slow but deep, the seeds
Of vengeance ripen into deeds,
Till, in some treacherous hour of calm,
They burst, like Zeilan's giant palm,
Whose buds fly open with a sound
That shakes the pigmy forests round !

Yes, Emir ! he who scaled that tower,
  And, had he reach'd thy slumbering breast,
Had taught thee, in a Gheber's power
  How safe even tyrant heads may rest —
Is one of many, brave as he,
Who loathe thy haughty race and thee ;

Who, though they know the strife is vain,
Who, though they know the riven chain
Snaps but to enter in the heart
Of him who rends its links apart,
Yet dare the issue, — blest to be
Even for one bleeding moment free,
And die in pangs of liberty!
Thou know'st them well, — 'tis some moons since
  Thy turban'd troops and blood-red flags,
Thou satrap of a bigot prince!
  Have swarm'd among these Green Sea crags;
Yet here, even here, a sacred band,
Ay, in the portal of that land
Thou, Arab, dar'st to call thy own,
Their spears across thy path have thrown;
Here — ere the winds half wing'd thee o'er —
Rebellion braved thee from the shore.

Rebellion! foul, dishonouring word,
  Whose wrongful blight so oft has stain'd
The holiest cause that tongue or sword
Of mortal ever lost or gain'd!
How many a spirit, born to bless,
  Hath sunk beneath that withering name,
Whom but a day's, an hour's, success
  Had wafted to eternal fame!
As exhalations, when they burst
From the warm earth, if chill'd at first,
If check'd in soaring from the plain,
Darken to fogs and sink again;
But, if they once triumphant spread

Their wings above the mountain-head,
Become enthroned in upper air,
And turn to sun-bright glories there !

And who is he that wields the might
    Of freedom on the Green Sea brink,
Before whose sabre's dazzling light
    The eyes of Yemen's warriors wink !
Who comes embower'd in the spears
Of Kerman's hardy mountaineers, —
Those mountaineers that truest, last
    Cling to their country's ancient rites,
As if that God, whose eyelids cast
    Their closing gleams on Iran's heights,
Among her snowy mountains threw
The last light of his worship too !

'Tis Hafed, — name of fear, whose sound
    Chills like the muttering of a charm ; —
Shout but that awful name around,
    And palsy shakes the manliest arm.
'Tis Hafed, most accurst and dire
(So rank'd by Moslem hate and ire)
Of all the rebel Sons of Fire !
Of whose malign, tremendous power
The Arabs, at their mid-watch hour,
Such tales of fearful wonder tell,
That each affrighted sentinel
Pulls down his cowl upon his eyes,
Lest Hafed in the midst should rise !
A man, they say, of monstrous birth,

A mingled race of flame and earth,
Sprung from those old, enchanted kings,
  Who, in their fairy helms, of yore,
A feather from the mystic wings
  Of the Simoorgh resistless wore;
And gifted by the Fiends of Fire,
Who groan'd to see their shrines expire,
With charms that, all in vain withstood,
Would drown the Koran's light in blood!

Such were the tales that won belief,
  And such the colouring fancy gave
To a young, warm, and dauntless Chief, —
  One who, no more than mortal brave,
Fought for the land his soul adored,
  For happy homes, and altars free, —
His only talisman, the sword;
  His only spell-word, Liberty!
One of that ancient hero line,
Along whose glorious current shine
Names that have sanctified their blood;
As Lebanon's small mountain flood
Is render'd holy by the ranks
Of sainted cedars on its banks!

'Twas not for him to crouch the knee
Tamely to Moslem tyranny;
'Twas not for him, whose soul was cast
In the bright mould of ages past,
Whose melancholy spirit, fed
With all the glories of the dead,

Though framed for Iran's happiest years,
Was born among her chains and tears ! —
'Twas not for him to swell the crowd
Of slavish heads, that shrinking bow'd
Before the Moslem, as he pass'd,
Like shrubs beneath the poison-blast —
No : far he fled, — indignant fled
   The pageant of his country's shame ;
While every tear her children shed
   Fell on his soul, like drops of flame ;
And, as a lover hails the dawn

Of a first smile, so welcomed he
The sparkle of the first sword drawn
    For vengeance and for liberty !

But vain was valour, — vain the flower
Of Kerman, in that deathful hour,
Against Al Hassan's whelming power.
In vain they met him, helm to helm,
Upon the threshold of that realm
He came in bigot pomp to sway,
And with their corpses block'd his way, —
In vain — for every lance they raised,
Thousands around the conqueror blazed ;
For every arm that lined their shore,
Myriads of slaves were wafted o'er, —
A bloody, bold, and countless crowd,
Before whose swarm as fast they bow'd
As dates beneath the locust-cloud !

There stood — but one short league away
From old Harmozia's sultry bay —
A rocky mountain, o'er the Sea
Of Oman beetling awfully.
A last and solitary link
    Of those stupendous chains that reach
From the broad Caspian's reedy brink
    Down winding to the Green Sea beach.
Around its base the bare rocks stood,
Like naked giants, in the flood,
    As if to guard the gulf across ;
While, on its peak, that braved the sky,

A ruin'd temple tower'd, so high
    That oft the sleeping albatross
Struck the wild ruins with her wing,
And from her cloud-rock'd slumbering
Started — to find man's dwelling there
In her own silent fields of air !
Beneath, terrific caverns gave
Dark welcome to each stormy wave
That dash'd, like midnight revellers, in ;
And such the strange, mysterious din
At times throughout those caverns roll'd,
And such the fearful wonders told
Of restless sprites imprison'd there,
That bold were Moslem who would dare,
At twilight hour, to steer his skiff
Beneath the Gheber's lonely cliff.
On the land side, those towers sublime,
That seem'd above the grasp of Time,
Were sever'd from the haunts of men
By a wide, deep, and wizard glen,
So fathomless, so full of gloom,
    No eye could pierce the void between.
It seem'd a place where Gholes might come,
With their foul banquets from the tomb,
    And in its caverns feed unseen.
Like distant thunder, from below,
    The sound of many torrents came ;
Too deep for eye or ear to know
If 'twere the sea's imprison'd flow,
    Or floods of ever-restless flame.
For each ravine, each rocky spire,

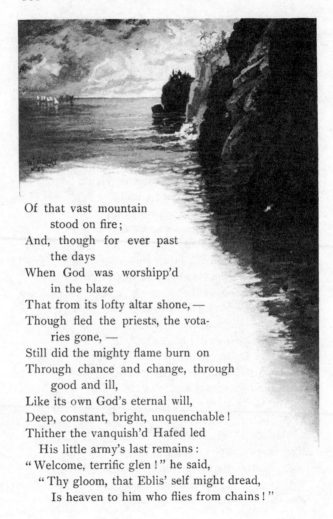

Of that vast mountain
    stood on fire;
And, though for ever past
    the days
When God was worshipp'd
    in the blaze
That from its lofty altar shone, —
Though fled the priests, the vota-
    ries gone, —
Still did the mighty flame burn on
Through chance and change, through
    good and ill,
Like its own God's eternal will,
Deep, constant, bright, unquenchable!
Thither the vanquish'd Hafed led
    His little army's last remains:
"Welcome, terrific glen!" he said,
    "Thy gloom, that Eblis' self might dread,
        Is heaven to him who flies from chains!"

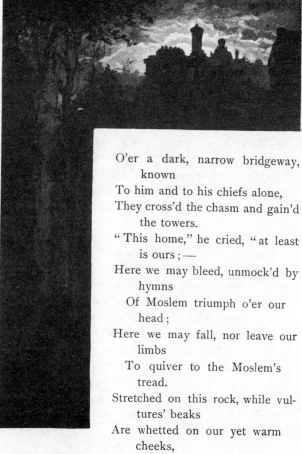

O'er a dark, narrow bridgeway,
    known
To him and to his chiefs alone,
They cross'd the chasm and gain'd
    the towers.
" This home," he cried, " at least
    is ours ; —
Here we may bleed, unmock'd by
    hymns
  Of Moslem triumph o'er our
    head ;
Here we may fall, nor leave our
    limbs
  To quiver to the Moslem's
    tread.
Stretched on this rock, while vul-
    tures' beaks
Are whetted on our yet warm
    cheeks,
Here, happy that no tyrant's eye
Gloats on our torments, we may die ! "

'Twas night when to those towers they came,
And gloomily the fitful flame
That from the ruin'd altar broke,
Glared on his features, as he spoke :
" 'Tis o'er, — what men could do, we've done:
If Iran *will* look tamely on,
And see her priests, her warriors, driven
    Before a sensual bigot's nod, —
A wretch, who takes his lusts to heaven,
    And makes a pander of his God ! —
If her proud sons, her high-born souls,
    Men in whose veins — oh, last disgrace ! —
The blood of Zal and Rustam rolls, —
    If they *will* court this upstart race,
And turn from Mithra's ancient ray,
To kneel at shrines of yesterday !
If they *will* crouch to Iran's foes, —
    Why, let them — till the land's despair
Cries out to heaven, and bondage grows
    Too vile for e'en the vile to bear !
Till shame at last, long hidden, burns
Their inmost core, and conscience turns
Each coward tear the slave lets fall
Back on his heart in drops of gall !
But *here*, at least, are arms unchain'd,
And souls that thraldom never stain'd ; —
    This spot, at least, no foot of slave
Or satrap ever yet profaned ;
    And though but few, though fast the wave
Of life is ebbing from our veins,
Enough for vengeance still remains.

As panthers, after set of sun,
Rush from the roots of Lebanon
Across the dark sea-robber's way,
We'll bound upon our startled prey ;
And when some hearts that proudest swell
Have felt our falchion's last farewell,
When hope's expiring throb is o'er,
And e'en despair can prompt no more,
This spot shall be the sacred grave
Of the last few who, vainly brave,
Die for the land they cannot save ! "
His chiefs stood round, each shining blade
Upon the broken altar laid ; —
And though so wild and desolate
Those courts where once the mighty sate,
Nor longer on those mouldering towers
Was seen the feast of fruits and flowers
With which of old the Magi fed
The wandering spirits of their dead ;
Though neither priest nor rites were there,
    Nor charmèd leaf of pure pomegranate,
Nor hymn, nor censer's fragrant air,
    Nor symbol of their worshipp'd planet ;
Yet the same God that heard their sires
Heard *them*, while on that altar's fires
They swore the latest, holiest deed
Of the few hearts still left to bleed
Should be, in Iran's injured name,
To die upon that Mount of Flame, —
The last of all her patriot line,
Before her last untrampled shrine !

Brave, suffering souls ! they little knew
How many a tear their injuries drew
From one meek maid, one gentle foe,
  Whom Love first touch'd with
      others' woe, —
  Whose life, as free from thought
      as sin,

        Slept like a
        lake, till
        Love threw
        in
        His talisman,
        and woke
        the tide,
        And spread its
        trembling
        circles wide.
        Once, Emir,
        thy unheed-
        ing child,
        'Mid all this
        havoc,
        bloom'd and
        smiled,—
    Tranquil as on some bat-
      tle-plain
    The Persian lily shines
      and towers,
Before the combat's reddening stain
  Hath fall'n upon her golden flowers.
Light-hearted maid, unawed, unmoved,

While heaven but spared the sire she loved,
Once at thy evening tales of blood
Unlistening and aloof she stood;
And oft, when thou hast paced along
    Thy haram halls with furious heat,
Hast thou not cursed her cheerful song,
    That came across thee, calm and sweet,
Like lutes of angels, touch'd so near
Hell's confines, that the damn'd can hear?

Far other feelings love hath brought, —
    Her soul all flame, her brow all sadness,
She now has but the one dear thought,
    And thinks that o'er, almost to madness!
Oft doth her sinking heart recall
    His words, — " for *my* sake weep for all ; "
And bitterly, as day on day
    Of revel carnage fast succeeds,
She weeps a lover snatch'd away
    In every Gheber wretch that bleeds.
There's not a sabre meets her eye
    But with his life-blood seems to swim;
There's not an arrow wings the sky
    But fancy turns its point to him.
No more she brings with footstep light
Al Hassan's falchion for the fight;
And, had he look'd with clearer sight,
Had not the mists that ever rise
From a foul spirit dimm'd his eyes,
He would have mark'd her shuddering frame,
When from the field of blood he came,

The faltering speech, the look estranged, —
Voice, step, and life, and beauty changed, —
He would have mark'd all this, and known
Such change is wrought by love alone!
Ah! not the love that should have bless'd
So young, so innocent a breast;
Not the pure, open, prosperous love,
That, pledged on earth, and seal'd above,
Grows in the world's approving eyes,
    In friendship's smile and home's caress,
Collecting all the heart's sweet ties
    Into one knot of happiness!
No, Hinda, no; — thy fatal flame
Is nursed in silence, sorrow, shame, —
    A passion, without hope or pleasure,
In thy soul's darkness buried deep,
    It lies like some ill-gotten treasure, —
Some idol, without shrine or name,
O'er which its pale-eyed votaries keep
Unholy watch, while others sleep!
Seven nights have darken'd Oman's Sea,
    Since last, beneath the moonlight ray,
She saw his light oar rapidly
    Hurry her Gheber's bark away;
And still she goes, at midnight hour,
To weep alone in that high bower,
And watch, and look along the deep
For him whose smiles first made her weep, —
But watching, weeping, all was vain,
She never saw his bark again.
The owlet's solitary cry;

The night-hawk, flitting darkly by;
  And oft the hateful carrion bird,
Heavily flapping his clogg'd wing,
Which reek'd with that day's banqueting, —
  Was all she saw, was all she heard.

'Tis the eighth morn — Al Hassan's brow
  Is brighten'd with unusual joy, —
What mighty mischief glads him now,
  Who never smiles but to destroy?
The sparkle upon Herkend's Sea,
When toss'd at midnight furiously,
Tells not of wreck and ruin nigh
More surely than that smiling eye!
" Up, daughter, up, — the kerna's breath
Has blown a blast would waken death,
And yet thou sleep'st, — up, child, and see
This blessed day for heaven and me,
A day more rich in Pagan blood
Than ever flash'd o'er Oman's flood.
Before another dawn shall shine,
His head — heart — limbs — will all be mine;
This very night his blood shall steep
These hands all over ere I sleep!" —
" *His* blood!" she faintly scream'd, — her mind
Still singling *one* from all mankind.
" Yes ; — spite of his ravines and towers,
Hafed, my child, this night is ours.
Thanks to all-conquering treachery,
  Without whose aid the links accursed,
That bind these impious slaves, would be

Too strong for Alla's self to burst!
That rebel fiend, whose blade has spread
My path with piles of Moslem dead,
Whose baffling spells had almost driven
Back from their course the Swords of Heaven,
This night, with all his band, shall know
How deep an Arab's steel can go,
When God and vengeance speed the blow.
And, Prophet! by that holy wreath
Thou wor'st on Ohod's field of death,
I swear, for every sob that parts
In anguish from these heathen hearts,
A gem from Persia's plunder'd mines
Shall glitter on thy shrine of shrines.
But ha! — she sinks — that look so wild —
Those livid lips — my child, my child,
This life of blood befits not thee,
And thou must back to Araby,
Ne'er had I risk'd thy timid sex
In scenes that man himself might dread,
Had I not hoped our every tread
Would be on prostrate Persians' necks —
Cursed race, they offer swords instead!
But cheer thee, maid, — the wind that now
Is blowing o'er thy feverish brow,
To-day shall waft thee from the shore;
And, ere a drop of this night's gore
Have time to chill in yonder towers,
Thou'lt see thy own sweet Arab bowers!"
His bloody boast was all too true:
There lurk'd one wretch among the few

Whom Hafed's eagle eye could count
Around him on that Fiery Mount, —
One miscreant, who for gold betray'd
The pathway through the valley's shade
To those high towers where Freedom stood
In her last hold of flame and blood.
Left on the field last dreadful night,
When, sallying from their sacred height,
The Ghebers fought hope's farewell fight,
He lay — but died not with the brave :
That sun, which should have gilt his grave,
Saw him a traitor and a slave ;
And while the few who thence return'd
To their high rocky fortress mourn'd
For him among the matchless dead
They left behind on glory's bed,
He lived, and in the face of morn
Laugh'd them and Faith and Heaven to scorn !
Oh for a tongue to curse the slave,
    Whose treason, like a deadly blight,
Comes o'er the councils of the brave,
    And blasts them in their hour of might !
May life's unblessèd cup for him
Be drugg'd with treacheries to the brim,
With hopes that but allure to fly,
    With joys that vanish while he sips, —
Like Dead-Sea fruits, that tempt the eye,
    But turn to ashes on the lips !
His country's curse, his children's shame,
Outcast of virtue, peace, and fame,
May he, at last, with lips of flame

On the parch'd desert thirsting die,
While lakes that shone in mockery nigh
Are fading off, untouch'd, untasted,
Like the once glorious hopes he blasted!
And when from earth his spirit flies,
   Just Prophet, let the damn'd one dwell
Full in the sight of Paradise,
   Beholding heaven, and feeling hell!

LALLA ROOKH had had
a dream, the night before,

which, in spite of the impending fate of poor Hafed,
made her heart more than usually cheerful during the
morning, and gave her cheeks all the freshened ani-
mation of a flower that the Bidmusk had just passed
over. She fancied that she was sailing on that Eastern ocean, where the sea-gypsies, who live for ever on
the water, enjoy a perpetual summer in wandering
from isle to isle, when she saw a small gilded bark
approaching her. It was like one of those boats which
the Maldivian islanders annually send adrift, at the
mercy of winds and waves, loaded with perfumes,
flowers, and odoriferous wood, as an offering to the
Spirit whom they call King of the Sea. At first this
little bark appeared to be empty, but on coming
nearer —

She had proceeded thus far in relating the dream
to her ladies, when Feramorz appeared at the door of
the pavilion. In his presence, of course, everything

else was forgotten, and the continuance of the story
was instantly requested by all. Fresh wood of aloes
was set to burn in the cassolets; the violet sherbets
were hastily handed round, and after a short prelude
on his lute, in the pathetic measure of Nava, which
is always used to express the lamentations of absent
lovers, the Poet thus continued :

THE day is lowering, — stilly black
Sleeps the grim wave, while heaven's rack,
Dispersed and wild, 'twixt earth and sky
Hangs like a shatter'd canopy !
There's not a cloud in that blue plain
     But tells of storm to come or past ; —
Here flying loosely as the mane
     Of a young war-horse in the blast ;
There roll'd in masses dark and swelling,
As proud to be the thunder's dwelling !
While some, already burst and riven,
Seem melting down the verge of heaven ;
As though the infant storm had rent
     The mighty womb that gave him birth,
And, having swept the firmament,
     Was now in fierce career for earth.

On earth, 'twas yet all calm around,
A pulseless silence, dread, profound,
More awful than the tempest's sound.
The diver steer'd for Ormus' bowers,
And moor'd his skiff till calmer hours ;
The sea-birds, with portentous screech,

Flew fast to land ; — upon the beach
The pilot oft had paused, with glance
Turn'd upward to that wild expanse ;
And all was boding, drear, and dark
As her own soul, when Hinda's bark
Went slowly from the Persian shore —
No music timed her parting oar,
Nor friends upon the lessening strand
Linger'd to wave the unseen hand,
Or speak the farewell heard no more ;
But lone, unheeded, from the bay
The vessel takes its mournful way,
Like some ill-destined bark that steers
In silence through the Gate of Tears.
And where was stern Al Hassan then ?
Could not that saintly scourge of men
From bloodshed and devotion spare
One minute for a farewell there ?
No ; — close within, in changeful fits
Of cursing and of prayer, he sits
In savage loneliness to brood
Upon the coming night of blood,
    With that keen second-scent of death,
By which the vulture snuffs his food
    In the still warm and living breath !
While o'er the wave his weeping daughter
Is wafted from these scenes of slaughter, —
As a young bird of Babylon,
Let loose to tell of victory won,
Flies home, with wing, ah ! not unstain'd
By the red hands that held her chain'd.

And does the long-left home she seeks
Light up no gladness on her cheeks?
The flowers she nursed, — the well-known groves,
Where oft in dreams her spirit roves, —
Once more to see her dear gazelles
Come bounding with their silver bells,

Her birds' new plu-
        mage to behold,
And the gay, gleam-
        ing fishes count,
She left, all filleted with
        gold,
Shooting around
        their jasper
        fount,—
Her little garden
        mosque to see,
And once again,
        at evening hour,
To tell her ruby
        rosary

In her own sweet acacia bower, —
Can these delights, that wait her now,
Call up no sunshine on her brow?
No ; — silent, from her train apart,
As if even now she felt at heart
The chill of her approaching doom,
She sits, all lovely in her gloom
As a pale angel of the grave ;
And o'er the wide tempestuous wave
Looks, with a shudder, to those towers
Where, in a few short awful hours,
Blood, blood, in steaming tides shall run,
Foul incense for to-morrow's sun !
"Where art thou, glorious stranger ! thou,

So loved, so lost, where art thou now?
Foe — Gheber — infidel — whate'er
Th' unhallow'd name thou'rt doom'd to bear,
Still glorious, — still to this fond heart
Dear as its blood, whate'er thou art!
Yes, — Alla, dreadful Alla! yes, —
If there be wrong, be crime in this,
Let the black waves, that round us roll,
Whelm me this instant, ere my soul,
Forgetting faith, home, father, — all, —
Before its earthly idol fall,
Nor worship even Thyself above him.
For, oh! so wildly do I love him
Thy Paradise itself were dim
And joyless, if not shared with him!"

Her hands were clasp'd, — her eyes upturn'd,
    Dropping their tears like moonlight rain;
And though her lip, fond raver! burn'd
    With words of passion, bold, profane,
Yet was there light around her brow,
    A holiness in those dark eyes,
Which show'd, — though wandering earthward
        now, —
    Her spirit's home was in the skies.
Yes, — for a spirit pure as hers
Is always pure, even while it errs;
As sunshine broken in the rill,
Though turn'd astray, is sunshine still!

So wholly had her mind forgot
All thoughts but one, she heeded not

The rising storm, — the wave that cast
A moment's midnight, as it pass'd, —
Nor heard the frequent shout, the tread
Of gathering tumult o'er her head, —
Clash'd swords, and tongues that seem'd to vie
With the rude riot of the sky.
But, hark! — that war-whoop on the deck, —
   That crash, as if each engine there,
Mast, sails, and all, were going to wreck,
   'Mid yells and stampings of despair!
Merciful Heaven! what *can* it be?
'Tis not the storm, though fearfully
The ship had shudder'd as she rode
O'er mountain waves.   " Forgive me, God!
Forgive me!" shriek'd the maid, and knelt,
Trembling all over, — for she felt
As if her judgment-hour was near;
While crouching round, half dead with fear,
Her handmaids clung, nor breathed, nor stirr'd —
When, hark! — a second crash — a third —
And now, as if a bolt of thunder
Had riven the labouring planks asunder,
The deck falls in, — what horrors then!
Blood, waves, and tackle, swords and men,
Come mix'd together through the chasm;
Some wretches in their dying spasm
Still fighting on, and some that call
" For God and Iran!" as they fall!

Whose was the hand that turn'd away
The perils of th' infuriate fray,

And snatch'd her breathless from beneath
This wilderment of wreck and death?
She knew not, — for a faintness came
Chill o'er her, and her sinking frame
Amid the ruins of that hour
Lay, like a pale and scorchèd flower,
Beneath the red volcano's shower!
But, oh! the sights and sounds of dread
That shock'd her, ere her senses fled!
The yawning deck, — the crowd that strove
Upon the tottering planks above, —
The sail, whose fragments, shivering o'er
The strugglers' heads, all dash'd with gore,
Flutter'd like bloody flags, — the clash
Of sabres, and the lightning's flash
Upon their blades, high toss'd about
Like meteor brands, — as if throughout
   The elements one fury ran,
One general rage, that left a doubt
   Which was the fiercer, Heaven or Man!
Once too — but no — it could not be —
   'Twas fancy all — yet once she thought
While yet her fading eyes could see,
   High on the ruin'd deck she caught
A glimpse of that unearthly form,
   That glory of her soul, — even then,
Amid the whirl of wreck and storm,
   Shining above his fellow men,
As, on some black and troublous night,
The Star of Egypt, whose proud light
Never hath beam'd on those who rest

In the White Islands of the West,
Burns through the storm with looks of flame
That put heaven's cloudier eyes to shame!
But no; — 'twas but the minute's dream, —
A fantasy, — and ere the scream
Had half-way pass'd her pallid lips,
A death-like swoon, a chill eclipse
Of soul and sense, its darkness spread
Around her, and she sunk, as dead!

How calm, how beautiful, comes on
The stilly hour, when storms are gone;
When warring winds have died away,
And clouds, beneath the dancing ray,
Melt off, and leave the land and sea
Sleeping in bright tranquillity —
Fresh as if day again were born,
Again upon the lap of Morn!
When the light blossoms, rudely torn
And scatter'd at the whirlwind's will,
Hang floating in the pure air still,
Filling it all with precious balm,
In gratitude for this sweet calm;
And every drop the thunder-showers
Have left upon the grass and flowers
Sparkles, as 'twere the lightning gem
Whose liquid flame is born of them!
    When, 'stead of one unchanging breeze,
There blow a thousand gentle airs,
And each a different perfume bears, —
    As if the loveliest plants and trees

Had vassal breezes of their own
To watch and wait on them alone,
And waft no other breath than theirs!
When the blue waters rise and fall,
In sleepy sunshine mantling all ;
And even that swell the tempest leaves
Is like the full and silent heaves
Of lovers' hearts, when newly blest,
Too newly to be quite at rest !

Such was the golden hour that broke
Upon the world when Hinda woke
From her long trance, and heard around
No motion but the water's sound
Rippling against the vessel's side,
As slow it mounted o'er the tide. —
But where is she ? — her eyes are dark,
Are wilder'd still, — is this the bark,
The same, that from Harmozia's bay
Bore her at morn, — whose bloody way
The sea-dog tracks ? — no ; strange and new
Is all that meets her wondering view.
Upon a galliot's deck she lies,
　　Beneath no rich pavilion's shade,
No plumes to fan her sleeping eyes,
　　Nor jasmine on her pillow laid.
But the rude litter, roughly spread
With war cloaks, is her homely bed,
And shawl and sash, on javelins hung,
For awning o'er her head are flung.
Shuddering she look'd around, — there lay

A group of warriors in the sun
Resting their limbs, as for that day
    Their ministry of death were done.
Some gazing on the drowsy sea,
Lost in unconscious reverie ;
And some, who seem'd but ill to brook
That sluggish calm, with many a look
To the slack sail impatient cast,
As loose it flagg'd around the mast.

Blest Alla ! who shall save her now ?
    There's not in all that warrior-band
One Arab sword, one turban'd brow
    From her own faithful Moslem land.
Their garb — the leathern belt that wraps
    Each yellow vest — that rebel hue —
The Tartar fleece upon their caps —
    Yes — yes — her fears are all too true.
And Heaven hath, in this dreadful hour,
Abandon'd her to Hafed's power, —
Hafed, the Gheber ! — at the thought
    Her very heart's blood chills within ;
He, whom her soul was hourly taught
    To loathe, as some foul fiend of sin,
Some minister, whom Hell had sent
To spread its blast, where'er he went,
And fling, as o'er our earth he trod,
His shadow betwixt man and God !
And she is now his captive, — thrown
In his fierce hands, alive, alone ;
His the infuriate band she sees,

All infidels — all enemies !
What was the daring hope that then
Cross'd her like lightning, as again,
With boldness that despair had lent,
  She darted through that armèd crowd
A look so searching, so intent,
  That e'en the sternest warrior bow'd
Abash'd, when he her glances caught,
As if he guessed whose form they sought.
But no, — she sees him not, —'tis gone :
The vision that before her shone
Through all the maze of blood and storm,
Is fled ; 'twas but a phantom form, —

One of those pass-
      ing, rainbow
      dreams,
Half light, half
      shade, which
      fancy's beams
Paint on the fleeting
      mists that roll
In trance or slumber
      round the soul!

But now the bark,
      with livelier
      bound,
  Scales the blue
      wave; the
      crew's in mo-
      tion;
The oars are out,
      and with light
      sound
  Break the bright
      mirror of the
      ocean,

Scattering its brilliant fragments round.
And now she sees — with horror sees —
   Their course is toward that mountain hold, —
Those towers, that make her life-blood freeze,
Where Mecca's godless enemies
   Lie, like beleaguer'd scorpions, roll'd
   In their last deadly, venomous fold!
Amid th' illumined land and flood
Sunless that mighty mountain stood;
Save where, above its awful head,
There shone a flaming cloud, blood-red,
As 'twere the flag of destiny
Hung out to mark where death would be!

Had her bewilder'd mind the power
Of thought in this terrific hour,
She well might marvel where or how
Man's foot could scale that mountain's brow;
Since ne'er had Arab heard or known
Of path but through the glen alone.
But every thought was lost in fear,
When, as their bounding bark drew near
The craggy base, she felt the waves
Hurry them towards those dismal caves
That from the deep in windings pass
Beneath that mount's volcanic mass;
And loud a voice on deck commands
To lower the mast and light the brands!
Instantly o'er the dashing tide
Within a cavern's mouth they glide,
Gloomy as that eternal porch

Through which departed spirits go; —
Not e'en the flare of brand and torch
   Its flickering light could further throw
   Than the thick flood that boil'd below.
Silent they floated; as if each
Sat breathless, and too awed for speech
In that dark chasm, where even sound
Seem'd dark, — so sullenly around
The goblin echoes of the cave
Mutter'd it o'er the long black wave,
As 'twere some secret of the grave!
But soft — they pause — the current turns
   Beneath them from its onward track.
Some mighty, unseen barrier spurns
   The vexed tide, all foaming, back,
And scarce the oar's redoubled force
Can stem the eddy's whirling course;
When, hark! — some desperate foot has sprung
Among the rocks, — the chain is flung, —
The oars are up, — the grapple clings,
And the toss'd bark in moorings swings.
Just then a daybeam through the shade
Broke tremulous; but ere the maid
Can see from whence the brightness steals,
Upon her brow she shuddering feels
A viewless hand, that promptly ties
A bandage round her burning eyes;
While the rude litter where she lies,
Uplifted by the warrior throng,
O'er the steep rocks is borne along.

Blest power of sunshine ! genial Day,
What balm, what life, is in thy ray !
To feel thee is such real bliss,
That had the world no joy but this,
To sit in sunshine calm and sweet, —
It were a world too exquisite
For man to leave it for the gloom,
The deep, cold shadow of the tomb !
E'en Hinda, though she saw not where
    Or whither wound the perilous road,
Yet knew by that awakening air
    Which suddenly around her glow'd,
That they had risen from darkness then,
And breathed the sunny world again !
But soon this balmy freshness fled ;
For now the steepy labyrinth led
Through damp and gloom, — 'mid crash of boughs
And fall of loosen'd crags that rouse
The leopard from his hungry sleep,
    Who, starting, thinks each crag a prey,
And long is heard from steep to steep,
    Chasing them down their thundering way !
The jackal's cry, — the distant moan
Of the hyena, fierce and lone ;
And that eternal, saddening sound
    Of torrents in the glen beneath,
As 'twere the ever-dark profound
    That rolls beneath the Bridge of Death !
All, all is fearful, — e'en to see,
    To gaze on those terrific things
She now but blindly hears, would be

    Relief to her imaginings!
Since never yet was shape so dread,
    But fancy, thus in darkness thrown,
And by such sounds of horror fed,
    Could frame more dreadful of her own.

But does she dream? Has fear again
Perplex'd the workings of her brain,
Or did a voice, all music, then
Come from the gloom, low whispering near, —
"Tremble not, love, thy Gheber's here?"
She *does* not dream, — all sense, all ear,
She drinks the words, "Thy Gheber's here."
'Twas his own voice, — she could not err, —
    Throughout the breathing world's extent
There was but *one* such voice for her,
    So kind, so soft, so eloquent!
Oh! sooner shall the rose of May
    Mistake her own sweet nightingale,
And to some meaner minstrel's lay
    Open her bosom's glowing veil,
Than love shall ever doubt a tone,
    A breath, of the beloved one!

Though blest, 'mid all her ills, to think
    She has that one beloved near,
Whose smile, though met on ruin's brink,
    Hath power to make e'en ruin dear, —
Yet soon this gleam of rapture, cross'd
By fears for him, is chill'd and lost.
How shall the ruthless Hafed brook

That one of Gheber blood should look,
With aught but curses in his eye,
On her, — a maid of Araby, —
A Moslem maid, — the child of him
    Whose bloody banner's dire success
Hath left their altars cold and dim,
    And their fair land a wilderness!
And, worse than all, that night of blood
    Which comes so fast — oh! who shall stay
The sword that once hath tasted food
    Of Persian hearts, or turn its way?
What arm shall then the victim cover,
Or from her father shield her lover?
" Save him, my God!" she inly cries, —
" Save him this night; and if thine eyes
    Have ever welcomed with delight
The sinner's tears, the sacrifice
    Of sinners' hearts, guard him this night,
And here, before thy throne, I swear
From my heart's inmost core to tear
    Love, hope, remembrance, though they be
Link'd with each quivering life-string there,
    And give it bleeding all to Thee!
Let him but live, the burning tear,
The sighs, so sinful, yet so dear,
Which have been all too much his own,
Shall from this hour be Heaven's alone.
Youth pass'd in penitence, and age
In long and painful pilgrimage,
Shall leave no traces of the flame
That wastes me now, — nor shall his name

E'er bless my lips, but when I pray
For his dear spirit, that away
Casting from its angelic ray
Th' eclipse of earth, he too may shine
Redeem'd, all-glorious and all thine!
Think — think what victory to win
One radiant soul like his from sin, —
One wandering star of virtue back
To its own native, heavenward track!
Let him but live, and both are thine,
 Together thine, — for, bless'd or cross'd,
Living or dead, his doom is mine,
 And if *he* perish, both are lost!"

THE next evening Lalla Rookh was entreated by
her ladies to continue the relation of her wonderful
dream; but the fearful interest that hung round the
fate of Hinda and her lover had completely removed
every trace of it from her mind; — much to the
disappointment of a fair seer or two in her train,
who prided themselves on their skill in interpreting
visions, and who had already remarked, as an unlucky omen, that the Princess, on the very morning
after the dream, had worn a silk dyed with the
blossoms of the sorrowful tree, Nilica.

Fadladeen, whose wrath had more than once broken
out during the recital of some parts of this most
heterodox poem, seemed at length to have made
up his mind to the infliction; and took his seat
this evening with all the patience of a martyr, while

the Poet continued his profane and seditious story
thus :

To tearless eyes and hearts at ease
The leafy shores and sun-bright seas,
That lay beneath the mountain's height,
Had been a fair, enchanting sight.
'Twas one of those ambrosial eves
A day of storm so often leaves
At its calm setting, — when the west
Opens her golden bowers of rest,
And a moist radiance from the skies
Shoots trembling down, as from the eyes
Of some meek penitent, whose last,
Bright hours atone for dark ones past,
And whose sweet tears, o'er wrong forgiven,
Shine, as they fall, with light from heaven !

'Twas stillness all, — the winds that late
    Had rush'd through Kerman's almond groves,
And shaken from her bowers of date
    That cooling feast the traveller loves,
Now, lull'd to languor, scarcely curl
    The Green Sea wave, whose waters gleam
Limpid, as if her mines of pearl
    Were melted all to form the stream;
And her fair islets, small and bright,
    With their green shores reflected there,
Look like those Peri isles of light,
    That hang by spell-work in the air.

But vainly did these
glories burst
On Hinda's dazzled eyes,
when first
The bandage from her brow
was taken,
And pale and awed as those
who waken
In their dark tombs, — when,
scowling near,
The Searchers of the grave
appear, —
She shuddering turn'd to read
her fate
In the fierce eyes
that flash'd around,

And saw those towers all desolate,
That o'er her head terrific frown'd,
As if defying e'en the smile

Of that soft heaven to gild their pile.
In vain, with mingled hope and fear,
She looks for him whose voice so dear
Had come, like music, to her ear —
Strange, mocking dream ! again 'tis fled,
And, oh ! the shoots, the pangs, of dread
That through her inmost bosom run.
    When voices from without proclaim
"Hafed, the Chief," — and, one by one,
    The warriors shout that fearful name !
He comes, — the rock resounds his tread, —
How shall she dare to lift her head,
Or meet those eyes, whose scorching glare
Not Yemen's boldest sons can bear ?
In whose red beam, the Moslem tells,
Such rank and deadly lustre dwells,
As in those hellish fires that light
The mandrake's charnel leaves at night !
How shall she bear that voice's tone,
At whose loud battle-cry alone
Whole squadrons oft in panic ran,
Scatter'd, like some vast caravan,.
When, stretch'd at evening round the well,
They hear the thirsting tiger's yell.

Breathless she stands, with eyes cast down,
Shrinking beneath the fiery frown
Which, fancy tells her, from that brow
Is flashing o'er her fiercely now ;
And shuddering, as she hears the tread
    Of his retiring warrior band.

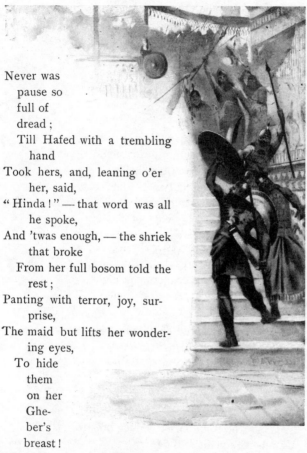

Never was
    pause so
    full of
    dread ;
    Till Hafed with a trembling
        hand
Took hers, and, leaning o'er
        her, said,
" Hinda ! " — that word was all
        he spoke,
And 'twas enough, — the shriek
        that broke
    From her full bosom told the
        rest ;
Panting with terror, joy, sur-
        prise,
The maid but lifts her wonder-
        ing eyes,
    To hide
        them
        on her
        Ghe-
        ber's
        breast !
'Tis he, 'tis he, — the man of blood,
The fellest of the Fire-fiend's brood,
Hafed, the demon of the fight,

Whose voice unnerves, whose glances blight,
Is her own lovèd Gheber, mild
And glorious as when first he smiled
In her lone tower, and left such beams
Of his pure eye to light her dreams,
That she believed her bower had given
Rest to some wanderer from heaven!

Moments there are, and this was one,
Snatch'd like a minute's gleam of sun
Amid the black simoom's eclipse, —
    Or like those verdant spots that bloom
Around the crater's burning lips,
    Sweetening the very edge of doom!
The past, — the future, — all that fate
Can bring of dark or desperate
Around such hours, but makes them cast
Intenser radiance while they last!

E'en he, this youth, — though dimm'd and gone
Each star of hope that cheer'd him on, —
His glories lost, his cause betray'd,
Iran, his dear-loved country, made
A land of carcasses and slaves,
One dreary waste of chains and graves!
Himself but lingering, dead at heart,
    To see the last, long-struggling breath
Of Liberty's great soul depart,
    Then lay him down, and share her death, —
E'en he, so sunk in wretchedness,
    With doom still darker gathering o'er him,

Yet in this moment's pure caress,
  In the mild eyes that shone before him.
Beaming that blest assurance, worth
All other transports known on earth,
That he was loved, — well, warmly loved, —
Oh! in this precious hour he proved
How deep, how thorough-felt the glow
Of rapture, kindling out of woe; —
How exquisite one single drop
Of bliss, thus sparkling to the top
Of misery's cup, — how keenly quaff'd,
Though death must follow on the draught!

She too, while gazing on those eyes
  That sink into her soul so deep,
Forgets all fears, all miseries,
  Or feels them like the wretch in sleep,
Whom fancy cheats into a smile,
Who dreams of joy, and sobs the while!

The mighty ruins where they stood,
  Upon the mount's high, rocky verge,
Lay open towards the ocean flood,
  Where lightly o'er th' illumined surge
Many a fair bark that, all the day,
Had lurk'd in sheltering creek or bay,
Now bounded on and gave their sails,
Yet dripping, to the evening gales;
Like eagles, when the storm is done,
Spreading their wet wings in the sun.
The beauteous clouds, though daylight's star
Had sunk behind the hills of Lar,

Were still with lingering glories bright, —
As if, to grace the gorgeous west,
   The Spirit of departing Light
That eve had left its sunny vest
   Behind him, ere he wing'd his flight.
Never was scene so form'd for love!
Beneath them waves of crystal move
In silent swell, heaven glows above;
And their pure hearts, to transport given,
Swell like the wave, and glow like heaven!
But, ah! too soon that dream is past;
   Again, again her fear returns; —
Night, dreadful night, is gathering fast,
   More faintly the horizon burns,
And every rosy tint that lay

On the smooth sea hath died away.
Hastily to the darkening skies
A glance she casts, then wildly cries :
" ' At night,' he said — and, look, 'tis near —
   Fly, fly — if yet thou lov'st me, fly —
Soon will his murderous band be here,
   And I shall see thee bleed and die.
Hush ! — heard'st thou not the tramp of men
Sounding from yonder fearful glen ! —
Perhaps e'en now they climb the wood —
   Fly, fly — though still the west is bright,
He'll come — oh ! yes — he wants thy blood —
   I know him — he'll not wait for night ! "

In terrors e'en to agony
   She clings around the wondering Chief ; —
" Alas, poor wilder'd maid ! to me
   Thou ow'st this raving trance of grief.
Lost as I am, nought ever grew
Beneath my shade but perish'd too, —
My doom is like the Dead-Sea air,
And nothing lives that enters there !
Why were our barks together driven
Beneath this morning's furious heaven ?
Why, when I saw the prize that chance
   Had thrown into my desperate arms, —
When, casting but a single glance
   Upon thy pale and prostrate charms,
I vow'd (though watching viewless o'er
   Thy safety through that hour's alarms)
To meet th' unmanning sight no more, —

Why have I broke that heart-wrung vow?
Why weakly, madly, met thee now? —
Start not, — that noise is but the shock
   Of torrents through yon valley hurl'd;
Dread nothing here, — upon this rock
   We stand above the jarring world,
Alike beyond its hope, its dread,
In gloomy safety, like the dead!
Or, could e'en earth and hell unite
In league to storm this sacred height,
Fear nothing now, — myself, to-night,
And each o'erlooking star that dwells
Near God, will be thy sentinels;
And, ere to-morrow's dawn shall glow,
Back to thy sire — "
                         " To-morrow! — no,"
The maiden scream'd, — " thou'lt never see
To-morrow's sun — death, death will be
The night-cry through each reeking tower,
Unless we fly, ay, fly this hour!
Thou art betray'd — some wretch who knew
That dreadful glen's mysterious clew —
Nay, doubt not — by yon stars, 'tis true —
Hath sold thee to my vengeful sire;
This morning, with that smile so dire
He wears in joy, he told me all,
And stamp'd in triumph through our hall,
As though thy heart already beat
Its last life-throb beneath his feet!
Good Heaven, how little dream'd I then
   His victim was my own loved youth! —

Fly — send — let some one watch the glen
  By all my hopes of heaven, 'tis truth!"
Oh! colder than the wind that freezes
  Founts that but now in sunshine play'd,
Is that congealing pang which seizes
  The trusting bosom when betray'd.
He felt it — deeply felt — and stood,
As if the tale had frozen his blood,
  So mazed and motionless was he;
Like one whom sudden spells enchant,
Or some mute, marble habitant
  Of the still Halls of Ishmonie!

But soon the painful chill was o'er,
And his great soul, herself once more,
Look'd from his brow in all the rays
Of her best, happiest, grandest days!
Never, in moment most elate,
  Did that high spirit loftier rise;
While bright, serene, determinate,
  His looks are lifted to the skies,
As if the signal-lights of fate
  Were shining in those awful eyes!
'Tis come, — his hour of martyrdom
In Iran's sacred cause is come;
And though his life hath pass'd away
Like lightning on a stormy day,
Yet shall his death-hour leave a track
  Of glory, permanent and bright,
To which the brave of after-times,
The suffering brave, shall long look back

With proud regret, and by its light
Watch through the hours of slavery's night
For vengeance on th' oppressor's crimes!
This rock, his monument aloft,
    Shall speak the tale to many an age;
And hither bards and heroes oft
    Shall come in secret pilgrimage,
And bring their warrior sons, and tell
The wondering boys where Hafed fell,
And swear them on those lone remains
Of their lost country's ancient fanes,
Never — while breath of life shall live
Within them — never to forgive
Th' accursèd race, whose ruthless chain
Hath left on Iran's neck a stain
Blood, blood alone can cleanse again!

Such are the swelling thoughts that now
Enthrone themselves on Hafed's brow;
And ne'er did saint of Issa gaze
    On the red wreath, for martyrs twined,
More proudly than the youth surveys
    That pile, which through the gloom behind
Half lighted by the altar's fire,
Glimmers, — his destined funeral pyre!
Heap'd by his own, his comrades' hands,
    Of every wood of odorous breath,
There, by the Fire-God's shrine it stands,
    Ready to fold in radiant death
The few still left of those who swore
To perish there, when hope was o'er, —

The few, to whom that couch of flame,
Which rescues them from bonds and shame,
Is sweet and welcome as the bed
For their own infant Prophet spread,
When pitying Heaven to roses turn'd
The death-flames that beneath him burn'd!
With watchfulness the maid attends
His rapid glance, where'er it bends —
Why shoot his eyes such awful beams?
What plans he now? what thinks or dreams?
Alas! why stands he musing here,
When every moment teems with fear?
"Hafed, my own beloved lord,"
She kneeling cries, — " first, last adored!
If in that soul thou'st ever felt
    Half what thy lips impassion'd swore,
Here, on my knees that never knelt
    To any but their God before,
I pray thee, as thou lov'st me, fly —
Now, now — ere yet their blades are nigh.
Oh, haste — the bark that bore me hither
    Can waft us o'er yon darkening sea
East — west — alas, I care not whither
    So thou art safe, and I with thee!
Go where we will, this hand in thine,
    Those eyes before me smiling thus,
Through good and ill, through storm and shine,
    The world's a world of love for us!
On some calm, blessed shore we'll dwell,
Where 'tis no crime to love too well, —
Where thus to worship tenderly

An erring child of light like thee
Will not be sin; or, if it be,
Where we may weep our faults away
Together kneeling, night and day, —
Thou, for *my* sake, at Alla's shrine,
And I — at *any* God's, for thine!"

Wildly these passionate words she spoke,
    Then hung her head, and wept for shame;
Sobbing, as if a heart-string broke
    With every deep-heaved sob that came.
While he, young, warm — oh! wonder not
    If for a moment pride and fame,
    His oath, his cause, that shrine of flame,
And Iran's self are all forgot
For her whom at his feet he sees
Kneeling in speechless agonies.
No, blame him not, if Hope awhile
Dawn'd in his soul, and threw her smile
O'er hours to come, — o'er days and nights
Wing'd with those precious, pure delights
Which she, who bends all beauteous there,
Was born to kindle and to share!

A tear or two, which, as he bow'd
    To raise the suppliant, trembling stole,
First warn'd him of this dangerous cloud
    Of softness passing o'er his soul.
Starting, he brush'd the drops away,
Unworthy o'er that cheek to stray; —
Like one who, on the morn of fight,

Shakes from his sword the dews of night,
That had but dimm'd, not stain'd, its light.
Yet, though subdued th' unnerving thrill,
Its warmth, its weakness, linger'd still,
   So touching in each look and tone,
That the fond, fearing, hoping maid
Half counted on the flight she pray'd,
   Half thought the hero's soul was grown
   As soft, as yielding as her own,
And smiled and bless'd him, while he said:
" Yes, — if there be some happier sphere
Where fadeless truth like ours is dear,
If there be any land of rest
   For those who love and ne'er forget,
Oh ! comfort thee, — for safe and blest
   We'll meet in that calm region yet ! "
Scarce had she time to ask her heart
If good or ill these words impart,
When the roused youth impatient flew
To the tower-wall, where, high in view,
A ponderous sea-horn hung, and blew
A signal, deep and dread as those
The storm-fiend at his rising blows.
Full well his chieftains, sworn and true
Through life and death, that signal knew;
For 'twas th' appointed warning-blast,
Th' alarm, to tell when hope was past
And the tremendous death-die cast !
And there, upon the mouldering tower,
Hath hung this sea-horn many an hour,
Ready to sound o'er land and sea

That dirge-note of the brave and free.
They came, — his chieftains at the call
Came slowly round, and with them all —
Alas! how few!—the worn remains
Of those who late o'er Kerman's plains
Went daily prancing to the clash

Of Moorish zel and tymbalon,
Catching new hope from every
flash
Of their long lances in the sun,
And, as their coursers charged the wind,
And the white ox-tails stream'd behind,
Looking as if the steeds they rode
Were wing'd, and every chief a god !

How fallen, how alter'd now ! how wan
Each scarred and faded visage shone,
As round the burning shrine they came ; —
How deadly was the glare it cast,
As mute they paused before the flame
To light their torches as they pass'd !

'Twas silence all, — the youth had plann'd
The duties of his soldier-band;
And each determined brow declares
His faithful chieftains well know theirs.

But minutes speed, — night gems the skies, —
And oh, how soon, ye blessed eyes
That look from heaven, ye may behold
Sights that will turn your star-fires cold!
Breathless with awe, impatience, hope,
The maiden sees the veteran group
Her litter silently prepare,
     And lay it at her trembling feet; —
And now the youth, with gentle care,
     Hath placed her in the shelter'd seat,
And press'd her hand, — that lingering press
     Of hands, that for the last time sever;
Of hearts, whose pulse of happiness,
     When that hold breaks, is dead for ever.
And yet to *her* this sad caress
     Gives hope, — so fondly hope can err!
'Twas joy, she thought, joy's mute excess, —
     Their happy flight's dear harbinger;
'Twas warmth, assurance, tenderness, —
     'Twas anything but leaving her.

" Haste, haste!" she cried, "the clouds grow dark,
But still, ere night, we'll reach the bark;
And by to-morrow's dawn — oh, bliss! —
     With thee upon the sun-bright deep,
Far off, I'll but remember this,

As some dark vanish'd dream of sleep !
And thou — "   But ha ! he answers not —
    Good Heaven ! — and does she go alone ?
She now has reach'd that dismal spot
    Where, some hours since, his voice's tone
Had come to soothe her fears and ills,
Sweet as the angel Israfil's,
When every leaf on Eden's tree
Is trembling to his minstrelsy ;
Yet now — oh, now, he is not nigh —
    " Hafed ! my Hafed ! if it be
Thy will, thy doom, this night to die,
    Let me but stay to die with thee,
And I will bless thy loved name,
Till the last life-breath leave this frame.
Oh ! let our lips, our cheeks, be laid
But near each other while they fade ;
Let us but mix our parting breaths,
And I can die ten thousand deaths !
You too, who hurry me away
So cruelly, one moment stay —
    Oh ! stay — one moment is not much —
He yet may come — for *him* I pray —
Hafed ! dear Hafed ! " — all the way
    In wild lamentings, that would touch
A heart of stone, she shriek'd his name
To the dark woods, — no Hafed came.
No, hapless pair, you've look'd your last ;
    Your hearts should both have broken then :
The dream is o'er, your doom is cast, —
    You'll never meet on earth again !

Alas for him, who hears her cries!
  Still half-way down the steep he stands,
Watching with fix'd and feverish eyes
  The glimmer of those burning brands,
That down the rocks, with mournful ray,
Light all he loves on earth away!
Hopeless as they who far at sea
  By the cold moon have just consign'd
The corse of one, loved tenderly,
To the bleak flood they leave behind;
And on the deck still lingering stay,
And long look back, with sad delay,
To watch the moonlight on the wave,
That ripples o'er that cheerless grave.

But see! he starts, — what heard he then?
That dreadful shout! — across the glen
From the land side it comes, and loud
Rings through the chasm; as if the crowd
Of fearful things that haunt that dell,
Its Gholes and Dives and shapes of hell,
Had all in one dread howl broke out,
So loud, so terrible that shout!
" They come, — the Moslems come!" he cries,
His proud soul mounting to his eyes;
" Now, spirits of the brave, who roam
Enfranchised through yon starry dome,
Rejoice, — for souls of kindred fire
Are on the wing to join your choir!"
He said; and, light as bridegrooms bound
  To their young loves, reclimb'd the steep

And gain'd the shrine : his chiefs stood round, —
   Their swords, as with instinctive leap,
Together, at that cry accursed,
Had from their sheaths, like sunbeams, burst.
And hark ! — again, again it rings ;
Near and more near its echoings
Peal through the chasm ; — oh ! who that then
Had seen those listening warrior men,
With their swords grasp'd, their eyes of flame
Turn'd on their Chief, could doubt the shame,
Th' indignant shame, with which they thrill
To hear those shouts and yet stand still ?
He read their thoughts, — they were his own, —
   " What ! while our arms can wield these
        blades,
Shall we die tamely, die alone, —
   Without one victim to our shades,
One Moslem heart, where, buried deep,
The sabre from its toil may sleep ?
No — God of Iran's burning skies !
Thou scorn'st th' inglorious sacrifice.
No — though of all earth's hopes bereft,
Life, swords, and vengeance still are left.
We'll make yon valley's reeking caves
   Live in the awe-struck minds of men
Till tyrants shudder when their slaves
   Tell of the Gheber's bloody glen.
Follow, brave hearts ! this pile remains
Our refuge still from life and chains ;
But his the best, the holiest bed,
Who sinks entomb'd in Moslem dead ! "

Down the precipitous rocks they sprung,
While vigour, more than human, strung
Each arm and heart.   Th' exulting foe
Still through the dark defiles below,
Track'd by his torches' lurid fire,
    Wound slow, as through Golconda's vale
The mighty serpent, in his ire,
    Glides on with glittering, deadly trail.
No torch the Ghebers need, — so well
They know each mystery of the dell,
    So oft have, in their wanderings,
Cross'd the wild race that round them dwell,
The very tigers from their delves
    Look out, and let them pass, as things
Untamed and fearless like themselves !

There was a deep ravine, that lay
Yet darkling in the Moslem's way, —
Fit spot to make invaders rue
The many fallen before the few.
The torrents from that morning's sky
Had fill'd the narrow chasm breast-high,
And on each side, aloft and wild,
Huge cliffs and toppling crags were piled, —
The guards with which young Freedom lines
The pathways to her mountain shrines.
Here, at this pass, the scanty band
Of Iran's last avengers stand ;
Here wait, in silence like the dead,
And listen for the Moslems' tread
So anxiously, the carrion bird
Above them flaps his wings unheard !

They come, — that plunge into the water
Gives signal for the work of slaughter.
Now, Ghebers, now, — if e'er your blades
  Had point or prowess, prove them now!
Woe to the file that foremost wades!
  They come, — a falchion greets each brow,
And as they tumble, trunk on trunk,
Beneath the gory waters sunk,
Still o'er their drowning bodies press
New victims quick and numberless;
Till scarce an arm in Hafed's band,
  So fierce their toil, hath power to stir,
But listless from each crimson hand
  The sword hangs, clogg'd with massacre.
Never was horde of tyrants met
With bloodier welcome, — never yet
To patriot vengeance hath the sword
More terrible libations pour'd!
All up the dreary, long ravine,
By the red, murky glimmer seen
Of half-quench'd brands, that o'er the flood
Lie scatter'd round and burn in blood,
What ruin glares! what carnage swims!
Heads, blazing turbans, quivering limbs,
Lost swords that, dropp'd from many a hand,
In that thick pool of slaughter stand, —
Wretches who, wading, half on fire
  From the toss'd brands that round them fly,
'Twixt flood and flame in shrieks expire;
  And some who, grasp'd by those that die,
Sink woundless with them, smother'd o'er

In their dead brethren's gushing gore!
But vainly hundreds, thousands bleed,
Still hundreds, thousands more succeed;
Countless as towards some flame at night
The north's dark insects wing their flight,
And quench or perish in its light,
To this terrific spot they pour,
Till, bridged with Moslem bodies o'er,
It bears aloft their slippery tread,
And o'er the dying and the dead —
Tremendous causeway! — on they pass.
Then, hapless Ghebers, then, alas!
    What hope was left for you? — for you,
Whose yet warm pile of sacrifice
Is smoking in their vengeful eyes, —
    Whose swords how keen, how fierce, they
        knew,
    And burn with shame to find how few.
Crush'd down by that vast multitude,
Some found their graves where first they
        stood;
While some with hardier struggle died,
And still fought on by Hafed's side,
Who, fronting to the foe, trod back
Towards the high towers his gory track;
And as a lion swept away
    By sudden swell of Jordan's pride
From the wild covert where he lay,
    Long battles with th' o'erwhelming tide,
So fought he back with fierce delay,
And kept both foes and fate at bay!

But whither now? their track is lost,
   Their prey escaped, — guide, torches gone, —
By torrent-beds and labyrinths cross'd,
   The scatter'd crowd rush blindly on.
" Curse on those tardy lights that wind,"
They panting cry, " so far behind, —
Oh for a bloodhound's precious scent,
To track the way the Gheber went!"
Vain wish, — confusedly along
They rush, more desperate as more wrong;
Till, wilder'd by the far-off lights
Yet glittering up those gloomy heights,
Their footing, mazed and lost, they miss,
And down the darkling precipice
Are dash'd into the deep abyss,
Or midway hang, impaled on rocks,
A banquet, yet alive, for flocks
Of ravening vultures, while the dell
Re-echoes with each horrible yell.

Those sounds — the last to vengeance dear,
That e'er shall ring in Hafed's ear —
Now reach'd him, as aloft, alone,
Upon the steep way, breathless thrown,
He lay beside his reeking blade,
   Resign'd, as if life's task were o'er,
Its last blood-offering amply paid,
   And Iran's self could claim no more.
One only thought, one lingering beam,
Now broke across his dizzy dream
Of pain and weariness, — 'twas she,

His heart's pure planet, shining yet
Above the waste of memory
　　When all life's other lights were set.
And never to his mind before
Her image such enchantment wore.
It seem'd as if each thought that stain'd,
　　Each fear that chill'd, their loves was past,
And not one cloud of earth remain'd
　　Between him and her glory cast; —
As if to charms before so bright,
　　New grace from other worlds was given,
And his soul saw her by the light
　　Now breaking o'er itself from heaven!

A voice spoke near him, — 'twas the tone
Of a loved friend, the only one
Of all his warriors, left with life
From that short night's tremendous strife:
" And must we then, my Chief, die here! —
Foes round us, and the shrine so near!"
These words have roused the last remains
　　Of life within him — " What! not yet
Beyond the reach of Moslem chains!"
　　The thought could e'en make Death forget
His icy bondage, — with a bound
He springs, all bleeding, from the ground,
And grasps his comrade's arm, now grown
E'en feebler, heavier, than his own,
And up the painful pathway leads,
Death gaining on each step he treads.
Speed them, thou God, who heard'st their vow!

They mount — they bleed — oh ! save them now ! —
The crags are red they've clamber'd o'er,
The rock-weed's dripping with their gore —
Thy blade, too, Hafed, false at length,
Now breaks beneath thy tottering strength —
Haste, haste, — the voices of the Foe
Come near and nearer from below —
One effort more — thank Heaven ! 'tis past;
They've gain'd the topmost steep at last,
And now they touch the temple's walls,
    Now Hafed sees the Fire divine —
When, lo ! his weak, worn comrade falls
    Dead on the threshold of the shrine.
" Alas, brave soul, too quickly fled !
    And must I leave thee withering here,
The sport of every ruffian's tread,
    The mark for every coward's spear ?
No, by yon altar's sacred beams ! "
He cries, and with a strength that seems
Not of this world, uplifts the frame
Of the fallen chief, and towards the flame
Bears him along ; — with death-damp hand
    The corpse upon the pyre he lays,
Then lights the consecrated brand,
    And fires the pile, whose sudden blaze
Like lightning bursts o'er Oman's Sea.
" Now, Freedom's God ! I come to thee,"
The youth exclaims, and with a smile
Of triumph vaulting on the pile,
In that last effort, ere the fires
Have harm'd one glorious limb, expires !

What shriek was that on Oman's tide?
  It came from yonder drifting bark,
That just has caught upon her side
  The death-light, and again is dark.
It is the boat — ah, why delay'd? —
That bears the wretched Moslem maid;
Confided to the watchful care
  Of a small veteran band, with whom
Their generous Chieftain would not share
  The secret of his final doom;
But hoped when Hinda, safe and free,
  Was render'd to her father's eyes,
Their pardon, full and prompt, would be
  The ransom of so dear a prize.
Unconscious, thus, of Hafed's fate,
And proud to guard their beauteous freight,
Scarce had they clear'd the surfy waves
That foam around those frightful caves,
When the curst war-whoops, known so well,
Came echoing from the distant dell.
Sudden each oar, upheld and still,
  Hung dripping o'er the vessel's side,
And, driving at the current's will,
  They rock'd along the whispering tide,
While every eye, in mute dismay,
  Was toward that fatal mountain turn'd,
Where the dim altar's quivering ray
  As yet all lone and tranquil burn'd.

Oh! 'tis not, Hinda, in the power
  Of fancy's most terrific touch

To paint thy pangs in that dread hour, —
   Thy silent agony : 'twas such
As those who feel could paint too well,
But none e'er felt and lived to tell !
'Twas not alone the dreary state
Of a lorn spirit, crush'd by fate,
When, though no more remains to dread,
   The panic chill will not depart ;
When, though the inmate Hope be dead,
   Her ghost still haunts the mouldering heart.
No — pleasures, hopes, affections gone,
The wretch may bear, and yet live on ;
Like things within the cold rock found
Alive when all's congeal'd around.
But there's a blank repose in this,
A calm stagnation, that were bliss ,
To the keen, burning, harrowing pain,
Now felt through all thy breast and brain, —
That spasm of terror, mute, intense, —
That breathless, agonized suspense,
From whose hot throb, whose deadly aching,
The heart hath no relief but breaking !

Calm is the wave, — heaven's brilliant lights
   Reflected dance beneath the prow.
Time was when, on such lovely nights,
   She who is there, so desolate now,
Could sit all cheerful, though alone,
   And ask no happier joy than seeing
The starlight o'er the waters thrown ;
No joy but that to make her blest,

And the fresh, buoyant sense of being
That bounds in youth's yet careless breast, —
Itself a star, not borrowing light,
But in its own glad essence bright.
How different now ! — but, hark ! again
The yell of havoc rings — brave men !
In vain with beating hearts ye stand
On the bark's edge ; in vain each hand
Half draws the falchion from its sheath :
    All's o'er, — in rust your blades may lie ; —
He at whose word they've scattered death
    E'en now, this night himself must die !
Well may ye look to yon dim tower,
    And ask, and wondering guess what means
The battle-cry at this dead hour.
    Ah ! she could tell you, — she who leans
Unheeded there, pale, sunk, aghast,
With brow against the dew-cold mast :
    Too well she knows, — her more than life,
Her soul's first idol and its last,
    Lies bleeding in that murderous strife.

But see — what moves upon the height ?
Some signal ! — 'tis a torch's light.
    What bodes its solitary glare ?
In gasping silence towards the shrine
All eyes are turn'd, — thine, Hinda, thine
    Fix their last failing life-beams there.
'Twas but a moment, — fierce and high
The death-pile blazed into the sky,
And far away o'er rock and flood

Its melancholy radiance sent;
While Hafed, like a vision, stood
Reveal'd before the burning pyre,
Tall, shadowy, like a Spirit of Fire
　　Shrined in its own grand element!
" 'Tis he!" the shuddering maid exclaims, —
　　But, while she speaks, he's seen no more;
High burst in air the funeral flames,
　　And Iran's hopes and hers are o'er!
One wild, heart-broken shriek she gave;

　　Than sprung as if to reach that blaze,
　　Where still she fix'd her dying gaze,
And gazing sunk into the wave, —
Deep, deep, — where never care or pain
Shall reach her innocent heart again!

Farewell, farewell to thee, Araby's daughter!
　　(Thus warbled a Peri beneath the dark sea.)
No pearl ever lay under Oman's green water
　　More pure in its shell than thy spirit in thee.

Oh! fair as the sea-flower close to thee growing,
　　How light was thy heart till love's witchery came,

Like the wind of the south o'er a summer lute blowing,
    And hush'd all its music, and wither'd its frame !

But long, upon Araby's green sunny highlands,
    Shall maids and their lovers remember the doom
Of her who lies sleeping among the Pearl Islands,
    With nought but the sea-star to light up her tomb.

And still, when the merry date-season is burning,
    And calls to the palm groves the young and the old,
The happiest there, from their pastime returning
    At sunset, will weep when thy story is told.

The young village maid, when with flowers she dresses
    Her dark flowing hair for some festival day,
Will think of thy fate, till, neglecting her tresses,
    She mournfully turns from the mirror away.

Nor shall Iran, beloved of her hero ! forget thee, —
    Though tyrants watch over her tears as they start,
Close, close by the side of that hero she'll set thee,
    Embalm'd in the innermost shrine of her heart.

Farewell — be it ours to embellish thy pillow
    With everything beauteous that grows in the deep ;
Each flower of the rock and each gem of the billow
    Shall sweeten thy bed and illumine thy sleep.

Around thee shall glisten the loveliest amber
    That ever the sorrowing sea-bird has wept ;
With many a shell, in whose hollow-wreathed chamber
    We, Peris of Ocean, by moonlight have slept.

We'll dive where the gardens of coral lie darkling,
    And plant all the rosiest stems at thy head ;
We'll seek where the sands of the Caspian are
        sparkling,
    And gather their gold to strew over thy bed.

Farewell — farewell — until pity's sweet fountain
    Is lost in the hearts of the fair and the brave,
They'll weep for the Chieftain who died on that
        mountain,
    They'll weep for the Maiden who sleeps in this
        wave.

THE singular placidity with which Fadladeen had
listened, during the latter part of this obnoxious story,
surprised the Princess and Feramorz exceedingly, and
even inclined towards him the hearts of these unsus-
picious young persons, who little knew the source of a
complacency so marvellous. The truth was, he had
been organising, for the last few days, a most notable
plan of persecution against the Poet, in consequence of
some passages that had fallen from him on the second
evening of recital, — which appeared to this worthy

Chamberlain to contain language and principles for which nothing short of the summary criticism of the chabuk would be advisable. It was his intention, therefore, immediately on their arrival at Cashmere, to give information to the King of Bucharia of the very dangerous sentiments of his minstrel; and if, unfortunately, that monarch did not act with suitable vigour on the occasion (that is, if he did not give the chabuk to Feramorz and a place to Fadladeen), there would be an end, he feared, of all legitimate government in Bucharia. He could not help, however, auguring better both for himself and the cause of potentates in general; and it was the pleasure arising from these mingled anticipations that diffused such unusual satisfaction through his features, and made his eyes shine out, like poppies of the desert, over the wild and lifeless wilderness of that countenance.

Having decided upon the Poet's chastisement in this manner, he thought it but humanity to spare him the minor tortures of criticism. Accordingly, when they assembled next evening in the pavilion, and Lalla Rookh expected to see all the beauties of her bard melt away, one by one, in the acidity of criticism, like pearls in the cup of the Egyptian queen, he agreeably disappointed her by merely saying, with an ironical smile, that the merits of such a poem deserved to be tried at a much higher tribunal; and then suddenly passing off into a panegyric upon all Mussulman sovereigns, more particularly his august and imperial master, Aurungzebe, — the wisest and best of the descendants of Timur, — who, among

other great things he had done for mankind, had
given to him (Fadladeen) the profitable posts of
Betel-carrier and Taster of Sherbets to the Emperor,
Chief Holder of the Girdle of Beautiful Forms, and
Grand Nazir, or Chamberlain of the Haram.

They were now not far from that forbidden river
beyond which no pure Hindoo can pass, and were
reposing for a time in the rich valley of Hussun
Abdaul, which had always been a favourite resting-
place of the Emperors in their annual migrations to
Cashmere. Here often had the Light of the Faith,
Jehan-Guire, wandered with his beloved and beautiful
Nourmahal; and here would Lalla Rookh have been
happy to remain for ever, giving up the throne of
Bucharia and the world for Feramorz and love in this
sweet lonely valley. The time was now fast approaching when she must see him no longer, or see him with
eyes whose every look belonged to another; and there
was a melancholy preciousness in these last moments,
which made her heart cling to them as it would to life.
During the latter part of the journey, indeed, she had
sunk into a deep sadness, from which nothing but the
presence of the young minstrel could awake her. Like
those lamps in tombs, which only light up when the
air is admitted, it was only at his approach that her
eyes became smiling and animated. But here, in this
dear valley, every moment was an age of pleasure;
she saw him all day, and was, therefore, all day happy,
— resembling, she often thought, the people of Zinge,
who attribute the unfading cheerfulness they enjoy to
one genial star that rises nightly over their heads.

The whole party, indeed, seemed in their liveliest mood during the few days they passed in this delightful solitude. The young attendants of the Princess, who were here allowed a freer range than they could safely be indulged with in a less sequestered place, ran wild among the gardens, and bounded through the meadows lightly as young roes over the aromatic plains of Tibet. While Fadladeen, besides the spiritual comfort he derived from a pilgrimage to the tomb of the saint from whom the valley is named, had opportunities of gratifying, in a small way, his taste for victims, by putting to death some hundreds of those unfortunate little lizards, which all pious Mussulmans make it a point to kill, — taking for granted that the manner in which the creature hangs its head is meant as a mimicry of the attitude in which the faithful say their prayers !

About two miles from Hussun Abdaul were those Royal Gardens, which had grown beautiful under the care of so many lovely eyes, and were beautiful still, though those eyes could see them no longer. This place, with its flowers and its holy silence, interrupted only by the dipping of the wings of birds in its marble basins filled with the pure water of those hills, was to Lalla Rookh all that her heart could fancy of fragrance, coolness, and almost heavenly tranquillity, — as the Prophet said of Damascus, " it was too delicious ; " and here, in listening to the sweet voice of Feramorz, or reading in his eyes what he never dared to tell her, the most exquisite moments of her whole life were passed. One evening when they had been talking of the Sultana Nourmahal, — the Light of the Haram, who had so often wandered among these flowers, and fed with her own hands, in those marble basins, the small shining fishes of which she was so fond, — the youth, in order to delay the moment of separation, proposed to recite a short story, or rather rhapsody, of which this adored Sultana was the heroine. It related, he said, to the reconcilement of a sort of lovers' quarrel, which took place between her and the Emperor during a Feast of Roses at Cashmere ; and would remind the Princess of that difference between Haroun-al-Raschid and his fair mistress Marida, which was so happily made up by the soft strains of the musician Moussali. As the story was chiefly to be told in song, and Feramorz had unluckily forgotten his own lute in the valley, he borrowed the vina of Lalla Rookh's little Persian slave, and thus began :

THE LIGHT OF THE HAREM.

WHO has not heard of the Vale of
    Cashmere,
    With its roses the brightest that
      earth ever gave,
Its temples, and grottos, and fountains
    as clear
    As the love-lighted eyes that hang
      over their wave !

Oh ! to see it at sunset, — when warm
    o'er the Lake
    Its splendour at parting a summer eve
      throws,

Like a bride, full of blushes, when lingering to take
  A last look of her mirror at night ere she goes!
When the shrines through the foliage are gleaming
  half shown,
And each hallows the hour by some rites of its own.
Here the music of prayer from a minaret swells,
  Here the Magian his urn full of perfume is
    swinging,
And here, at the altar, a zone of sweet bells
  Round the waist of some fair Indian dancer is
    ringing.
Or to see it by moonlight, — when mellowly shines
The light o'er its palaces, gardens, and shrines;
When the waterfalls gleam like a quick fall of stars,
And the nightingale's hymn from the Isle of
  Chenars
Is broken by laughs and light echoes of feet
From the cool, shining walks where the young people
  meet.
Or at morn, — when the magic of daylight awakes
A new wonder each minute, as slowly it breaks,
Hills, cupolas, fountains, call'd forth every one
Out of darkness, as they were just born of the sun;
When the Spirit of Fragrance is up with the day,
From his haram of night-flowers stealing away,
And the wind, full of wantonness, woos like a lover
The young aspen-trees till they tremble all over;
When the East is as warm as the light of first hopes,
  And Day, with his banner of radiance unfurl'd,
Shines in through the mountainous portal that opes,
  Sublime, from that Valley of bliss to the world!

But never yet, by night or day,
In dew of spring or summer's ray,
Did the sweet Valley shine so gay
As now it shines, — all love and light,
Visions by day and feasts by night !
A happier smile illumes each brow,
    With quicker spread each heart uncloses,
And all is ecstasy; for now
    The Valley holds its Feast of Roses, —
That joyous time, when pleasures pour
Profusely round, and in their shower
Hearts open, like the season's rose,
    The floweret of a hundred leaves,
Expanding while the dew-fall flows,
    And every leaf its balm receives !

'Twas when the hour of evening came
    Upon the Lake, serene and cool ;
When Day had hid his sultry flame
    Behind the palms of Baramoule ;
When maids began to lift their heads,
Refresh'd, from their embroider'd beds,
Where they had slept the sun away,
And waked to moonlight and to play.
All were abroad, — the busiest hive
On Bela's hills is less alive
When saffron beds are full in flower,
Than look'd the Valley in that hour.
A thousand restless torches play'd
Through every grove and island shade ;
A thousand sparkling lamps were set

On every dome and minaret;
And fields and pathways, far and near,
Were lighted by a blaze so clear,
That you could see, in wandering round,
The smallest rose-leaf on the ground.
Yet did the maids and matrons leave
Their veils at home, that brilliant eve;
And there were glancing eyes about,
And cheeks, that would not dare shine out
In open day, but thought they might
Look lovely then, because 'twas night!
And all were free, and wandering,
  And all exclaim'd to all they met
That never did the summer bring
  So gay a Feast of Roses yet; —
The moon had never shed a light
  So clear as that which bless'd them there;
The roses ne'er shone half so bright,
  Nor they themselves look'd half so fair.

And what a wilderness of flowers!
It seem'd as though from all the bowers
And fairest fields of all the year
The mingled spoil were scatter'd here.
The lake too like a garden breathes,
  With the rich buds that o'er it lie, —
As if a shower of fairy wreaths
  Had fallen upon it from the sky!
And then the sounds of joy, — the beat
Of tabors and of dancing feet; —
The minaret-crier's chant of glee

Sung from his lighted gallery,
And answer'd by a ziraleet
From neighbouring haram, wild and sweet; —
The merry laughter, echoing
From gardens where the silken swing
Wafts some delighted girl above
The top leaves of the orange grove;
Or from those infant groups that play
Among the tents that line the way,
Flinging, unawed by slave or mother,
Handfuls of roses at each other! —
And the sounds from the Lake, — the low whisp'ring
    in boats,
    As they shoot through the moonlight; — the dip-
        ping of oars,
And the wild, airy warbling that everywhere floats,
    Through the groves round the islands, as if all the
        shores,
Like those of Kathay, utter'd music, and gave
An answer in song to the kiss of each wave!
But the gentlest of all are those sounds, full of feeling,
That soft from the lute of some lover are stealing, —
Some lover who knows all the heart-touching power
Of a lute and a sigh in this magical hour.
Oh! best of delights as it everywhere is
To be near the loved *One*, — what a rapture is his
Who in moonlight and music thus sweetly may glide
O'er the Lake of Cashmere with that *One* by his side!
If woman can make the worst wilderness dear,
Think, think what a heaven she must make of Cash-
        mere!

So felt the magnificent Son of Acbar,
When from power and pomp and the trophies of war
He flew to that Valley, forgetting them all
With the Light of the Haram, his young Nourmahal;
When free and uncrown'd as the conqueror roved
By the banks of that Lake with his only beloved,
He saw, in the wreaths she would playfully snatch
From the hedges, a glory his crown could not match,
And preferr'd in his heart the dear ringlet that curl'd
Down her exquisite neck, to the throne of the world!
There's the beauty, for ever unchangingly bright,
Like a long sunny lapse of a summer day's light,
Shining on, shining on, by no shadow made tender,
Till love falls asleep in the sameness of splendour:
This *was* not the beauty — oh! nothing like this,
That to young Nourmahal gave such magic of bliss;
But that loveliness, ever in motion, which plays
Like the light upon autumn's soft shadowy days,
Now here and now there, giving warmth as it flies
From the lips to the cheek, from the cheek to the eyes,
Now melting in mist and now breaking in gleams,
Like the glimpses a saint has of heaven in his dreams!
When pensive, it seem'd as if that very grace,
That charm of all others, was born with her face;
And when angry, — for e'en in the tranquillest climes
Light breezes will ruffle the flowers sometimes, —
The short, passing anger but seem'd to awaken
New beauty, like flowers that are sweetest when
     shaken.
If tenderness touch'd her, the dark of her eye
At once took a darker, a heavenlier dye,

From the depth of whose shadow, like holy revealings
From innermost shrines, came the light of her feelings!
Then her mirth — oh! 'twas sportive as ever took
    wing
From the heart with a burst, like the wild bird in
    spring; —
Illumed by a wit that would fascinate sages,
Yet playful as Peris just loosed from their cages.
While her laugh, full of life, without any control
But the sweet one of gracefulness, rung from her soul;
And where it most sparkled no glance could discover,
In lip, cheek, or eyes, for she brighten'd all over, —
Like any fair lake that the breeze is upon,
When it breaks into dimples and laughs in the sun.
Such, such were the peerless enchantments that gave
Nourmahal the proud Lord of the East for her slave;
And though bright was his haram, — a living parterre
Of the flowers of this planet, — though treasures were
    there,
For which Soliman's self might have given all the
    store
That the navy from Ophir e'er wing'd to his shore, —
Yet dim before *her* were the smiles of them all,
And the Light of his Haram was young Nourmahal!

But where is she now, this night of joy,
When bliss is every heart's employ?
  When all around her is so bright,
So like the visions of a trance,
That one might think, who came by chance
  Into the Vale this happy night,

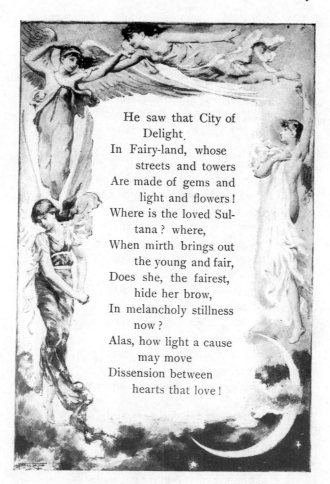

He saw that City of
Delight,
In Fairy-land, whose
streets and towers
Are made of gems and
light and flowers!
Where is the loved Sul-
tana? where,
When mirth brings out
the young and fair,
Does she, the fairest,
hide her brow,
In melancholy stillness
now?
Alas, how light a cause
may move
Dissension between
hearts that love!

Hearts that the world in vain had tied,
And sorrow but more closely tried;
That stood the storm, when waves were rough,
Yet in a sunny hour fall off,
Like ships that have gone down at sea,
When heaven was all tranquillity!
A something, light as air, — a look,
   A word unkind or wrongly taken, —
Oh! love, that tempests never shook,
   A breath, a touch, like this hath shaken.
And ruder words will soon rush in
To spread the breach that words begin;
And eyes forget the gentle ray
They wore in courtship's smiling day;
And voices lose their tone that shed
A tenderness round all they said,
Till fast declining, one by one,
The sweetnesses of love are gone,
And hearts so lately mingled seem
Like broken clouds, — or like the stream
That smiling left the mountain's brow,
   As though its waters ne'er could sever,
Yet, ere it reach the plain below,
   Breaks into floods that part for ever.

O you that have the charge of Love,
   Keep him in rosy bondage bound,
As in the fields of Bliss above
   He sits, with flowerets fetter'd round:
Loose not a tie that round him clings,
Nor ever let him use his wings;

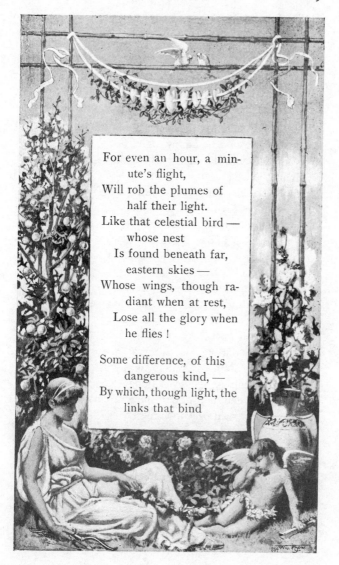

For even an hour, a min-
ute's flight,
Will rob the plumes of
half their light.
Like that celestial bird —
whose nest
Is found beneath far,
eastern skies —
Whose wings, though ra-
diant when at rest,
Lose all the glory when
he flies !

Some difference, of this
dangerous kind, —
By which, though light, the
links that bind

The fondest hearts may soon be riven ;
Some shadow in love's summer heaven,
Which, though a fleecy speck at first,
May yet in awful thunder burst ; —
Such cloud it is, that hangs over
The heart of the imperial lover,
And far hath banish'd from his sight
His Nourmahal, his Haram's Light !
Hence is it, on this happy night,
When Pleasure through the fields and groves
Has let loose all her world of loves,
And every heart has found its own, —
He wanders joyless and alone,
And weary as that bird of Thrace,
Whose pinion knows no resting-place.
In vain the loveliest cheeks and eyes
This Eden of the earth supplies
    Come crowding round, — the cheeks are pale
The eyes are dim ; though rich the spot
With every flower this earth has got,
    What is it to the nightingale,
If there his darling rose is not ?
In vain the Valley's smiling throng
Worship him, as he moves along ;
He heeds them not, — one smile of hers
Is worth a world of worshippers.
They but the star's adorers are,
She is the heaven that lights the star !

Hence is it too that Nourmahal,
    Amid the luxuries of this hour,

Far from the joyous festival,
  Sits in her own sequester'd bower,
With no one near, to soothe or aid,
But that inspired and wondrous maid,
Namouna, the enchantress, — one,
O'er whom his race the golden sun
For unremember'd years has run,
Yet never saw her blooming brow
Younger or fairer than 'tis now.
Nay, rather, as the west-wind's sigh
Freshens the flower it passes by,
Time's wing but seem'd, in stealing o'er,
To leave her lovelier than before.
Yet on her smiles a sadness hung,
And when, as oft, she spoke or sung
Of other worlds, there came a light
From her dark eyes so strangely bright,
That all believed nor man nor earth
Were conscious of Namouna's birth !

All spells and talismans she knew,
  From the great Mantra, which around
The Air's sublimer spirits drew,
  To the gold gems of Afric, bound
Upon the wandering Arab's arm,
To keep him from the Siltim's harm.
And she had pledged her powerful art,
Pledged it with all the zeal and heart
Of one who knew, though high her
      sphere,
What 'twas to lose a love so dear,

To find some spell that should recall
Her Selim's smile to Nourmahal!

  'Twas midnight, — through the lat-
    tice, wreathed
With woodbine, many a perfume
    breathed
From plants that wake when others
    sleep, —
From timid jasmine buds, that keep
Their odour to themselves all day,
But, when the sunlight dies away,
Let the delicious secret out
To every breeze that roams about ; —
When thus Namouna : " 'Tis the hour

That scatters spells on
    herb and flower,
And garlands might be gather'd
    now,
That, twined around the sleep-
    er's brow,
Would make him dream of such delights,
    Such miracles and dazzling sights,
As Genii of the Sun behold,
At evening, from their tents of gold,
Upon th' horizon, — where they play
Till twilight comes, and, ray by ray,
Their sunny mansions melt
        away!
Now, too, a chaplet might be
        wreathed
Of buds o'er which the moon
        has breathed,
Which worn by her, whose
        love has stray'd,
    Might bring some Peri from the skies,

Some sprite, whose very soul is made
   Of flowerets' breaths and lovers' sighs,
And who might tell — "
                     " For me, for me,"
Cried Nourmahal impatiently, —
" Oh ! twine that wreath for me to-night !"
Then rapidly, with foot as light
As the young musk-roe's, out she flew
To cull each shining leaf that grew
Beneath the moonlight's hallowing beams
For this enchanted Wreath of Dreams.
Anemones and Seas of Gold,
   And new-blown lilies of the river,
And those sweet flowerets, that unfold
   Their buds on Camadeva's quiver ;
The tuberose, with her silvery light,
   That in the gardens of Malay
Is call'd the mistress of the Night,
So like a bride, scented and bright,
   She comes out when the sun's away ;
Amaranths, such as crown the maids
That wander through Zamara's shades ;
And the white moon-flower, as it shows
On Serendib's high crags to those
Who near the isle at evening sail,
Scenting her clove-trees in the gale ; —
In short, all flowerets and all plants,
   From the divine Amrita tree,
That blesses heaven's inhabitants
   With fruits of immortality,
Down to the bazil tuft, that waves

Its fragrant blossom over graves,
   And to the humble rosemary,
Whose sweets so thanklessly are shed
To scent the desert and the dead, —
All in that garden bloom, and all
Are gather'd by young Nourmahal,
Who heaps her baskets with the flowers
   And leaves, till they can hold no more;
Then to Namouna flies, and showers
   Upon her lap the shining store.

With what delight th' Enchantress views
So many buds, bathed with the dews
And beams of that bless'd hour ! — her glance
   Spoke something, past all mortal pleasures,
As, in a kind of holy trance,
   She hung above those fragrant treasures,
Bending to drink their balmy airs,
As if she mix'd her soul with theirs.
And 'twas, indeed, the perfume shed
From flowers and scented flame that fed
Her charmèd life, — for none had e'er
Beheld her taste of mortal fare,
Nor ever in aught earthly dip,
But the morn's dew, her roseate lip.
Fill'd with the cool, inspiring smell,
Th' Enchantress now begins her spell,
Thus singing, as she winds and weaves
In mystic form the glittering leaves :

I know where the winged visions dwell
   That around the night-bed play ;

I know each herb and floweret's bell,
　　Where they hide their wings by day.
　　　　Then hasten we, maid,
　　　　　To twine our braid,
To-morrow the dreams and flowers will fade.

The image of love that nightly flies
　　To visit the bashful maid,
Steals from the jasmine flower, that sighs
　　Its soul, like her, in the shade.
The hope, in dreams, of a happier hour
　　That alights on misery's brow,
Springs out of the silvery almond-flower
　　That blooms on a leafless bough.
　　　　Then hasten we, maid,
　　　　　To twine our braid,
To-morrow the dreams and flowers will fade.

The visions that oft to worldly eyes
　　The glitter of mines unfold,
Inhabit the mountain-herb, that dyes
　　The tooth of the fawn like gold.
The phantom shapes — oh, touch not them —
　　That appall the murderer's sight,
Lurk in the fleshly mandrake's stem,
　　That shrieks, when torn at night !
　　　　Then hasten we, maid,
　　　　　To twine our braid,
To-morrow the dreams and flowers will fade.

The dream of the injured patient mind,
　　That smiles at the wrongs of men,

Is found in the bruised and wounded rind
    Of the cinnamon, sweetest then !
        Then hasten we, maid,
        To twine our braid,
To-morrow the dreams and flowers
    will fade.

No sooner was the flowery crown
Placed on her head, then sleep came
    down,
Gently as nights of summer fall,
Upon the lids of Nourmahal ;
And suddenly a tuneful breeze,
As full of small rich harmonies
As ever wind that o'er the tents
Of Azab blew, was full of scents,
Steals on her ear, and floats and
    swells,
    Like the first air of morning
        creeping
Into those wreathy, Red-
        Sea shells,

Where Love himself, of old, lay sleeping;
And now a spirit form'd, 'twould seem,
    Of music and of light, so fair,
So brilliantly his features beam,
    And such a sound is in the air
Of sweetness, when he waves his wings,
Hovers around her, and thus sings:

From Chindara's warbling fount I come,
    Call'd by that moonlight garland's spell;
From Chindara's fount, my fairy home,
    Where in music, morn and night, I dwell.
Where lutes in the air are heard about,
    And voices are singing the whole day long,
And every sigh the heart breathes out
    Is turn'd, as it leaves the lips, to song!
      Hither I come
      From my fairy home;
And if there's a magic in music strain,
      I swear by the breath
      Of that moonlight wreath,
Thy lover shall sigh at thy feet again!

For mine is the lay that lightly floats,
And mine are the murmuring, dying notes,
That fall as soft as snow on the sea,
And melt in the heart as instantly!

And the passionate strain that, deeply going,
    Refines the bosom it trembles through,
As the musk-wind, over the water blowing,
    Ruffles the waves, but sweetens it too!

Mine is the charm whose mystic sway
The Spirits of past Delight obey;
Let but the tuneful talisman sound,
And they come, like Genii, hovering round.

And mine is the gentle song that bears
    From soul to soul the wishes of love,
As a bird that wafts through genial airs
    The cinnamon seed from grove to grove.

'Tis I that mingle in one sweet measure
The past, the present, and future of pleasure;
When memory links the tone that is gone
    With the blissful tone that's still in the ear,
And hope from a heavenly note flies on
    To a note more heavenly still that is near!

The warrior's heart, when touch'd by me,
Can as downy soft and as yielding be
As his own white plume, that high amid death
Through the field has shone, yet moves with a
        breath.

And, oh, how the eyes of beauty glisten,
    When music has reach'd her inmost soul,
Like the silent stars, that wink and listen
    While heaven's eternal melodies roll!
            So hither I come
            From my fairy home,
    And if there's a magic in music strain,
            I swear by the breath
            Of that moonlight wreath,
    Thy lover shall sigh at thy feet again.

'Tis dawn, — at least that earlier dawn
Whose glimpses are again withdrawn,
As if the morn had waked, and then
Shut close her lids of light again.

And Nourmahal is up, and trying
    The wonders of her lute, whose strings —
Oh, bliss! — now murmur like the sighing
    From that ambrosial spirit's wings!

And then, her voice, — 'tis more than human, —
    Never, till now, had it been given
To lips of any mortal woman
    To utter notes so fresh from heaven;

Sweet as the breath of angel sighs,
    When angel sighs are most divine, —
"Oh! let it last till night," she cries,
    " And he is more than ever mine."
And hourly she renews the lay,
    So fearful lest its heavenly sweetness
Should, ere the evening, fade away, —
    For things so heavenly have such fleetness!
But, far from fading, it but grows
Richer, diviner, as it flows;
Till rapt she dwells on every string,
    And pours again each sound along,
Like Echo, lost and languishing
    In love with her own wondrous song.

That evening (trusting that his soul
    Might be from haunting love released

By birth, by music, and
the bowl)
Th' imperial Selim held a feast
In his magnificent Shalimar;
In whose saloons, when the first star
Of evening o'er the waters trembled,
The Valley's loveliest all assembled, —
All the bright creatures that, like dreams,
Glide through its foliage, and drink beams
Of beauty from its founts and streams;
And all those wandering minstrel-maids
Who leave — how *can* they leave? — the shades
Of that dear Valley, and are found
  Singing in gardens of the south
Those songs, that ne'er so sweetly sound
As from a young Cashmerian's
    mouth.

There too the haram's inmates smile; —
　　Maids from the west, with sun-bright hair,
And from the Garden of the Nile,
　　Delicate as the roses there;
Daughters of Love from Cyprus' rocks,
With Paphian diamonds in their locks;
Light Peri forms, such as there are
On the gold meads of Candahar;
And they before whose sleepy eyes,
　　In their own bright Kathaian bowers,
Sparkle such rainbow butterflies,
　　That they might fancy the rich flowers
That round them in the sun lay sighing,
Had been by magic all set flying!
Everything young, everything fair,
From east and west is blushing there,
Except — except — O Nourmahal!
Thou loveliest, dearest of them all,
The one whose smile shone out alone,
Amidst a world the only one!
Whose light, among so many lights,
Was like that star, on starry nights,

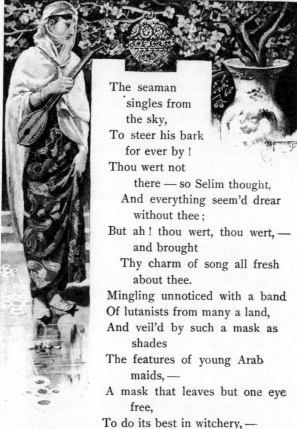

The seaman
  singles from
  the sky,
To steer his bark
  for ever by !
Thou wert not
    there — so Selim thought,
  And everything seem'd drear
    without thee ;
But ah ! thou wert, thou wert, —
    and brought
  Thy charm of song all fresh
    about thee.
Mingling unnoticed with a band
Of lutanists from many a land,
And veil'd by such a mask as
    shades
The features of young Arab
    maids, —
A mask that leaves but one eye
    free,
  To do its best in witchery, —
She roved, with beating heart, around,
  And waited, trembling, for the minute
When she might try if still the sound
  Of her loved lute had magic in it.

The board was spread with fruits and wine,
With grapes of gold, like those that shine
On Casbin's hills; — pomegranates full
   Of melting sweetness, and the pears
And sunniest apples that Caubul
   In all its thousand gardens bears;
Plantains, the golden and the green,
Malaya's nectar'd mangusteen;
Prunes of Bokara, and sweet nuts
   From the far groves of Samarcand,
And Basra dates, and apricots,
   Seed of the sun, from Iran's land; —
With rich conserve of Visna cherries,
Of orange flowers, and of those berries
That, wild and fresh, the young gazelles
Feed on in Erac's rocky dells.
All these in richest vases smile,
   In baskets of pure santal-wood
And urns of porcelain from that isle
   Sunk underneath the Indian flood,
Whence oft the lucky diver brings
Vases to grace the halls of kings.
Wines too, of every clime and hue,
Around their liquid lustre threw:
Amber Rosolli, — the bright dew
From vineyards of the Green Sea gushing;
And Shiraz wine, that richly ran
   As if that jewel, large and rare,
The ruby, for which Kublai-Khan
Offer'd a city's wealth, was blushing
   Melted within the goblets there !

And amply Selim quaffs of each,
And seems resolved the floods shall reach
His inward heart, — shedding around
 A genial deluge, as they run,
That soon shall leave no spot undrown'd,
 For Love to rest his wings upon.
He little knew how blest the boy
 Can float upon a goblet's streams,
Lighting them with his smile of joy ; —
 As bards have seen him, in their dreams,
Down the blue Ganges laughing glide
 Upon a rosy lotus wreath,
Catching new lustre from the tide
 That with his image shone beneath.
But what are cups without the aid
 Of song to speed them as they flow ?
And see — a lovely Georgian maid,
 With all the bloom, the freshen'd glow,
Of her own country maidens' looks,
When warm they rise from Teflis' brooks ;
And with an eye whose restless ray,
 Full, floating, dark, — oh, he who knows
His heart is weak, of heaven should pray
 To guard him from such eyes as those ! —
With a voluptuous wildness flings
Her snowy hand across the strings
Of a syrinda, and thus sings:

Come hither, come hither, — by night and by day,
 We linger in pleasures that never are gone ;
Like the waves of the summer, as one dies away,

Another as sweet and as
shining comes on.
And the love that is o'er, in expiring, gives birth
To a new one as warm, as un-
equall'd in bliss;
And, oh! if there be an elysium
on earth,
It is this, it is this.

Here maidens are sighing, and
fragrant their sigh
As the flower of the Amra just oped
by a bee;
And precious their tears as that rain
from the sky

Which turns into pearls as it falls in the sea.
Oh ! think what the kiss and the smile must be worth,
  When the sigh and the tear are so perfect in bliss;
And own if there be an elysium on earth,
      It is this, it is this !

Here sparkles the nectar that, hallow'd by love,
  Could draw down those angels of old from their
    sphere,
Who for wine of this earth left the fountains above,
  And forgot heaven's stars for the eyes we have
    here.
And, bless'd with the odour our goblet gives forth,
  What spirit the sweets of his Eden would miss?
For, oh! if there be an elysium on earth,
      It is this, it is this !

The Georgian's song was scarcely mute,
  When the same measure, sound for sound,
Was caught up by another lute,
  And so divinely breathed around,
That all stood hush'd and wondering,
  And turn'd and look'd into the air,
As if they thought to see the wing
  Of Israfil, the Angel, there; —
So powerfully on every soul
That new, enchanted measure stole.
While now a voice, sweet as the note
Of the charm'd lute, was heard to float
Along its chords, and so entwine
  Its sound with theirs, that none knew whether

The voice or lute was most divine,
    So wondrously they went together :

There's a bliss beyond all that the minstrel has told,
    When two, that are link'd in one heavenly tie,
With heart never changing and brow never cold,
    Love on through all ills, and love on till they die !
One hour of a passion so sacred is worth
    Whole ages of heartless and wandering bliss ;
And, oh ! if there *be* an elysium on earth,
        It is this, it is this !

    'Twas not the air, 'twas not the words,
    But that deep magic in the chords
    And in the lips, that gave such power
    As music knew not till that hour.
    At once a hundred voices said,
    " It is the mask'd Arabian maid ! "
    While Selim, who had felt the strain
    Deepest of any, and had lain
    Some minutes rapt, as in a trance,
        After the fairy sounds were o'er,
    Too inly touch'd for utterance,
        Now motion'd with his hand for more :

    Fly to the desert, fly with me !
    Our Arab tents are rude for thee ;
    But, oh ! the choice what heart can doubt
    Of tents with love, or thrones without ?

    Our rocks are rough, but smiling there
    Th' acacia waves her yellow hair,

Lonely and sweet, nor loved the less
For flowering in a wilderness.

Our sands are bare, but down their slope
The silvery-footed antelope
As gracefully and gayly springs
As o'er the marble courts of kings.

Then come — thy Arab maid will be
The loved and lone acacia-tree,
The antelope, whose feet shall bless
With their light sound thy loneliness.

Oh ! there are looks and tones that dart
An instant sunshine through the heart, —
As if the soul that minute caught
Some treasure it through life had sought;

As if the very lips and eyes
Predestined to have all our sighs,
And never be forgot again,
Sparkled and spoke before us then.

So came thy every glance and tone,
When first on me they breathed and shone
New as if brought from other spheres,
Yet welcomed as if loved for years !

Then fly with me, — if thou hast known
No other flame, nor falsely thrown
A gem away, that thou hadst sworn
Should ever in thy heart be worn.

Come, if the love thou hast for me
Is pure and fresh as mine for thee, —
Fresh as the fountain underground,
When first 'tis by the lapwing found.

But if for me thou dost forsake
Some other maid, and rudely break
Her worshipp'd image from its base,
To give to me the ruin'd place, —

Then fare thee well — I'd rather make
My bower upon some icy lake
When thawing suns begin to shine,
Than trust to love so false as thine!

There was a pathos in this lay,
    That, e'en without enchantment's art,
Would instantly have found its way
    Deep into Selim's burning heart;
But breathing, as it did, a tone
To earthly lutes and lips unknown,
With every chord fresh from the touch
Of Music's spirit, — 'twas too much!
Starting, he dash'd away the cup, —
Which, all the time of this sweet air,
His hand had held, untasted, up,
    As if 'twere fix'd by magic there, —
And naming her, so long unnamed,
So long unseen, wildly exclaim'd,
" O Nourmahal! O Nourmahal!
    Hadst thou but sung this witching strain,

I could forget — forgive thee all,
    And never leave those eyes
        again."

The mask is off — the charm is
        wrought —
And Selim to his heart has
        caught,
In blushes, more than ever
        bright,
His Nourmahal, his Haram's
        Light !
And well do vanish'd frowns
        enhance
The charm of every brighten'd
        glance ;
And dearer seems each dawn-
        ing smile

For having lost its light awhile ;
And, happier now for all her sighs
As on his arm her head reposes,
She whispers him, with laughing eyes,
"Remember, love, the Feast of Roses !"

FADLADEEN, at the conclusion of this light rhapsody, took occasion to sum up his opinion of the young Cashmerian's poetry, — of which, he trusted, they had that evening heard the last. Having recapitulated the epithets, "frivolous," "inharmonious," "nonsensical," he proceeded to say that, viewing it in the most favourable light, it resembled one of those Maldivian boats to which the Princess had alluded in the relation of her dream, — a slight, gilded thing, sent adrift without rudder or ballast, and with nothing but vapid sweets and faded flowers on board. The profusion, indeed, of flowers and birds which this Poet had ready on all occasions — not to mention dews, gems etc., — was a most oppressive kind of opulence to his hearers, and had the unlucky effect of giving to his style all the glitter of the flower-garden without its method, and all the flutter of the aviary without its song. In addition to this, he chose his subjects badly, and was always most inspired by the worst parts of them. The charms of paganism, the merits of rebellion, — these were the themes honoured with his particular enthusiasm ; and, in the poem just recited, one of his most palatable passages was in praise of that beverage of the Unfaithful, wine, — " being, perhaps," said he, relaxing into a smile, as conscious of his own character in the haram on this point, "one of those bards whose fancy owes all its illumination to the grape, like that painted porcelain, so curious and so rare, whose images are only visible when liquor is poured into it." Upon the whole, it was his opinion, from the specimens which they had heard, and which, he begged to say, were the most tiresome part of the journey, that, whatever other merits this well-dressed young gentleman might possess, poetry was by no means his proper avocation; "and indeed," concluded the critic, "from his fondness for flowers and for birds, I would venture to suggest that a florist or a bird-catcher is a much more suitable calling for him than a poet."

They had now begun to ascend those barren mountains which separate Cashmere from the rest of India; and as the heats were intolerable, and the time of their encampment limited to the few hours necessary for refreshment and repose, there was an end to all their delightful evenings, and Lalla Rookh saw no more of Feramorz. She now felt that her short dream of happiness was over, and that she had nothing but the recollection of its few blissful hours, like the one draught of sweet water that serves the camel across the wilderness, to be her heart's refreshment during the dreary waste of life that was before her. The blight that had fallen upon her spirit soon found its way to her cheek, and her ladies saw with regret — though not without some suspicion of the cause — that the beauty of their mistress, of which they were almost as proud as of their own, was fast vanishing away at the very moment of all when she had most need of it. What must the

King of
Bucharia feel,
when, instead of
the lively and beau-
tiful Lalla Rookh,
whom the Poets
of Delhi had de-
scribed as more
perfect than the
divinest images in
the House of Azor,
he should re-
ceive a pale

and inanimate victim, upon whose cheek neither health nor pleasure bloomed, and from whose eyes Love had fled, — to hide himself in her heart!

If anything could have charmed away the melancholy of her spirits, it would have been the fresh airs and enchanting scenery of that Valley, which the Persians so justly called the Unequalled. But neither the coolness of its atmosphere, so luxurious after toiling up those bare and burning mountains; neither the splendour of the minarets and pagodas, that shone out from the depth of its woods, nor the grottos, hermitages, and miraculous fountains which make every spot of that region holy ground; neither the countless waterfalls, that rush into the Valley from all those high and romantic mountains that encircle it, nor the fair city on the Lake, whose houses, roofed with flowers, appeared at a distance like one vast and variegated parterre; — not all these wonders and glories of the most lovely country under the sun could steal her heart for a minute from those sad thoughts, which but darkened and grew bitterer every step she advanced.

The gay pomps and processions that met her upon her entrance into the Valley, and the magnificence with which the roads all along were decorated, did honour to the taste and gallantry of the young King. It was night when they approached the city; and for the last two miles they had passed under arches, thrown from hedge to hedge, festooned with only those rarest roses from which the Attar Gul, more precious than gold, is distilled, and illuminated in rich and fanciful forms with lanterns of the triple-

coloured tortoise-shell of
Pegu. Sometimes, from
a dark wood by the side
of the road, a display of

fireworks would break out so sudden and so brilliant, that a Brahmin might think he saw that grove in whose purple shade the God of Battles was born, bursting into a flame at the moment of his birth; while, at other times, a quick and playful irradiation continued to brighten all the fields and gardens by which they passed, forming a line of dancing lights along the horizon, like the meteors of the north as they are seen by those hunters who pursue the white and blue foxes on the confines of the Icy Sea.

These arches and fireworks delighted the ladies of the Princess exceedingly; and, with their usual good logic, they deduced from his taste for illuminations that the King of Bucharia would make the most exemplary husband imaginable. Nor, indeed, could Lalla Rookh herself help feeling the kindness and splendour with which the young bridegroom welcomed her; but she also felt how painful is the gratitude which kindness from those we cannot love excites, and that their best blandishments come over the heart with all that chilling and deadly sweetness which we can fancy in the cold, odoriferous wind that is to blow over this earth in the last day.

The marriage was fixed for the morning after her arrival, when she was, for the first time, to be presented to the monarch in that imperial palace beyond the Lake, called the Shalimar. Though a night of more wakeful and anxious thought had never been passed in the Happy Valley before, yet when she rose in the morning and her ladies came round her, to assist in the adjustment of the bridal

ornaments, they thought they had never seen her
look half so beautiful. What she had lost of the
bloom and radiancy of her charms was more than
made up by that intellectual expression, that soul in
the eyes, which is worth all the rest of loveliness.
When they had tinged her fingers with the henna leaf,
and placed upon her brow a small coronet of jewels,
of the shape worn by the ancient Queens of Bucharia,
they flung over her head the rose-coloured bridal veil,
and she proceeded to the barge that was to convey
her across the Lake ; — first kissing, with a mournful
look, the little amulet of cornelian which her father
had hung about her neck at parting.

The morning was as fair as the maid upon whose
nuptials it rose ; and the shining Lake, all covered
with boats, the minstrels playing upon the shores of
the islands, and the crowded summer-houses on the
green hills around, with shawls and banners waving
from their roofs, presented such a picture of animated
rejoicing, as only she, who was the object of it all,
did not feel with transport. To Lalla Rookh alone
it was a melancholy pageant; nor could she have
even borne to look upon the scene, were it not for a
hope that, among the crowds around, she might once
more perhaps catch a glimpse of Feramorz. So
much was her imagination haunted by this thought
that there was scarcely an islet or boat she passed,
at which her heart did not flutter with a momentary
fancy that he was there. Happy, in her eyes, the
humblest slave upon whom the light of his dear looks
fell ! — In the barge immediately after the Princess

was Fadladeen, with his silken curtains thrown widely
apart, that all might have the benefit of his august
presence, and with his head full of the speech he was
to deliver to the King, " concerning Feramorz, and
literature, and the chabuk, as connected therewith."

They had now entered the canal which leads from
the Lake to the splendid domes and saloons of the
Shalimar, and glided on through gardens ascending
from each bank, full of flowering shrubs that made
the air all perfume ; while from the middle of the
canal rose jets of water, smooth and unbroken, to
such a dazzling height, that they stood like pillars
of diamond in the sunshine. After sailing under the
arches of various saloons, they at length arrived at
the last and most magnificent, where the monarch
awaited the coming of his bride ; and such was the
agitation of her heart and frame, that it was with dif-
ficulty she walked up the marble steps, which were
covered with cloth of gold for her ascent from the
barge. At the end of the hall stood two thrones, as
precious as the Cerulean Throne of Koolburga, on
one of which sat Aliris, the youthful King of Bucharia, and on the other was, in a few minutes, to be
placed the most beautiful Princess in the world.
Immediately upon the entrance of Lalla Rookh into
the saloon, the monarch descended from his throne
to meet her ; but scarcely had he time to take her
hand in his, when she screamed with surprise and
fainted at his feet. It was Feramorz himself that
stood before her ! — Feramorz was himself the Sov-
ereign of Bucharia, who in this disguise had accom-

panied his young bride from Delhi, and, having won her love as an humble minstrel, now amply deserved to enjoy it as a king.

The consternation of Fadladeen at this discovery was, for the moment, almost pitiable. But change of opinion is a resource too convenient in courts for this experienced courtier not to have learned to avail himself of it. His criticisms were all, of course, recanted instantly; he was seized with an admiration of the King's verses, as unbounded as, he begged him to believe, it was disinterested; and the following week saw him in possession of an additional place, swearing by all the saints of Islam that never had there existed so great a poet as the monarch, Aliris, and ready to prescribe his favourite regimen of the chabuk for every man, woman, and child that dared to think otherwise.

Of the happiness of the King and Queen of Bucharia, after such a beginning, there can be but little doubt; and, among the lesser symptoms, it is recorded of Lalla Rookh, that to the day of her death, in memmory of their delightful journey, she never called the King by any other name than Feramorz.